# Extensions in Reading™ Series

BOOK
3

CURRICULUM ASSOCIATES®, Inc.

## Acknowledgments

Product Development and Design by Chameleon Publishing Services
    Written by Susan A. DeStefano
    Illustrated by Leslie Alfred McGrath

## Credits

"This School Is for the Birds" is reprinted from the September 2001 issue of *Ranger Rick* magazine, with the permission of the publisher, the National Wildlife Federation. Copyright 2001 by the National Wildlife Federation.

"I Scream for Ice Cream" by Sarah Golland is used with permission of the author. Copyright 2001.

"The Coral Reef Crisis." Used with permission from *Time for Kids* magazine, © 2000, 2001.

"The Case of the Missing Flowers," "The Boy Who Loved Pizza," "The Lesson," and "The Garden" are reprinted with permission of Susan A. DeStefano. Copyright 2001.
ISBN 0-7609-1745-0
©2002—Curriculum Associates, Inc.
North Billerica, MA 01862
15 14 13 12 11 10 9 8 7 6 5 4 3 2

# Table of Contents

# Finding Main Idea

## Learn About Finding Main Idea

*Thinking about
the strategy*

If you know how to find the **main idea** when you read, you can better understand and enjoy what you read. The main idea is the most important idea of a paragraph or of a whole selection.

You will sometimes find the main idea of a paragraph in a main idea sentence. Then all the other sentences in the paragraph help explain the main idea. Sometimes, an author will not state, or say, the main idea in a main idea sentence. Then look at all the other sentences. Decide the one idea that the sentences all tell about.

| To find the main idea of a paragraph | To find the main idea of a selection |
|---|---|
| Look for a main idea sentence. It is often the first or last sentence in the paragraph. Figure out the most important idea that all the sentences make. Look at the title. | Look at the title. Look at the first and last paragraphs. The main idea is often found in the first or last paragraph. Think about the main ideas of all the paragraphs. |

*Studying a model*

Read the paragraph and the notes beside it.

*The first sentence states the main idea: The students planted a garden to help the animals.*

*All the other sentences help explain how the garden could help the animals.*

The students in Mrs. Becker's class decided to plant a small garden to help the animals that lived near their school. Hummingbirds and bees could come to gather nectar from the flowers. Small animals, like chipmunks and birds, could collect the seeds from some of the garden plants. Spiders could weave their webs among the leaves and stems. Other insects could also munch on the leaves.

# Learn About a Graphic Organizer

*Understanding a main idea chart*

A **main idea chart** will help you find and understand the main idea of a paragraph or selection. You can use a main idea chart when reading articles, essays, and other nonfiction works.

Here is a main idea chart for the paragraph on page 4. It shows the main idea and the details that help explain the main idea.

*Write the main idea sentence. If there is no main idea sentence, write a sentence that tells the main idea.*

| What is the main idea? | | | |
|---|---|---|---|
| The students in Mrs. Becker's class decided to plant a small garden to help the animals that lived near their school. | | | |

*List examples, reasons, and other details that give more information about the main idea.*

| What details help explain the main idea? | | | |
|---|---|---|---|
| Hummingbirds and bees could gather nectar. | Small animals could collect seeds from the garden. | Spiders could weave webs among leaves and stems. | Insects could munch on leaves. |

When you fill in a main idea chart, you see how an author arranges details in a paragraph or whole selection to explain an idea.

*What is the main idea that the author wants to make about the garden?* The first sentence states that the students decided to plant the garden to help the animals that lived near the school. The author then gives four examples of ways that the garden will help the animals.

**As you read, ask yourself**

- What is the main idea?
- Does the author state the main idea in a main idea sentence?
- What one idea do all the sentences in the paragraph help explain?

# Learn About a Form of Writing

*Focusing on a letter to the editor*

Readers write **letters to the editor** of a newspaper or a magazine to give their personal opinions about a subject. Sometimes a reader writes a letter to the editor to reach all the people in the community.

A letter to the editor often has these features.

- It tells a writer's opinions or feelings.
- It gives facts and details that support the writer's main idea.
- It uses business letter form.

Here is a letter to the editor of a school paper. As you read, think of what the writer wants readers to do or understand.

Dear Editor:

The Rose Elementary School math team deserves our thanks and praise. Last week, the team won first place in a statewide contest. Each team member stayed after school every day for months to study and practice. At the contest, everyone said how polite and friendly the team was. During the contest, the team members showed the true meaning of teamwork.

Sincerely,

Maria Peterson

*Organizing ideas in a main idea chart*

You can use a main idea chart when reading a letter to the editor. Here is a filled-in main idea chart for the letter above.

| What is the main idea? | | | |
|---|---|---|---|
| The Rose Elementary School math team deserves our thanks and praise. | | | |

| What details help explain the main idea? | | | |
|---|---|---|---|
| The team won first place in a state contest. | Team members stayed after school to study. | The team was polite and friendly. | The team showed the true meaning of teamwork. |

## Prepare for the Reading Selection

*Gaining knowledge*

When you think of school, you probably think of reading, writing, math, and of course, homework. All of these are an important part of learning, and school is all about learning. However, many schools also offer a variety of special programs that teach children other kinds of skills. These programs provide children with a chance to discover and develop hidden talents in areas such as sports, music, art, and theater. Many people believe that these special programs are important but not absolutely necessary to a child's education. As a result, when schools do not have enough money to support these programs, the programs are dropped. The letters to the editor that you will read on the pages that follow, focus on the special programs that make school more than just reading, writing, math, and homework to students.

## Learn Vocabulary

*Understanding vocabulary*

The boxed words below are **boldfaced** in the selection. Learn the meaning of each word. Then write the word that matches the clue.

| |
|---|
| attend |
| cancelled |
| overheard |
| instructor |
| tribute |
| appreciate |

1. This is an event to honor someone or something.

   _____

2. If you did this, you listened in on what someone was saying

   to someone else. _____

3. This is someone who teaches you a skill.

   _____

4. If a game was this, the game would not be played.

   _____

5. This means the opposite of "take for granted."

   _____

6. This means "to be present at." _____

Read the first letter to the editor.

1659 Poplar Avenue
Shelbyville, Missouri 55555
November 16, 2001

Letters to the Editor
*The Shelbyville Gazette*
23 Highland Street
Shelbyville, Missouri 55555

Dear Editor:

I am in third grade at Lincoln Elementary School. Every Thursday, I **attend** the after-school music program. I am learning to play the trumpet. Yesterday, I found out that the after-school music program might be **cancelled**. I am writing to say that the after-school music program should not be cancelled. After talking with many of my classmates and friends, I can say for sure that I am not the only one who feels this way.

Our class does have music during the regular school week. However, the after-school program is special. In music class, we sing songs and listen to music. At the after-school program, we learn how to play real instruments.

I have been taking trumpet lessons every Thursday afternoon for ten weeks. I never thought I would be able to play any instrument. I admit that, at first, I was terrible. My parents would smile as I practiced, but I really think that they wanted to cover their ears. Now, however, I can play two songs that actually sound like music. I **overheard** my father tell my mother that Mr. Portland, my **instructor**, must be a magician as well as a musician.

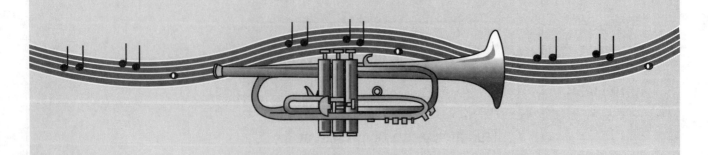

Playing a musical instrument is important to me for many reasons. It offers me the chance to express myself. Practicing has taught me the rewards of hard work. Music has also improved my self-confidence. I used to be scared in front of a crowd. Now I am proud and eager to play my trumpet for any size audience.

The after-school music program has also given me the chance to make new friends. I have made friends with students in the fourth and fifth grade who also play the trumpet. And of course, Mr. Portland is a friend to all of us.

The after-school music program is important and fun. It should not be cancelled.

Thank you,

*Joanna MacDougal*
Joanna MacDougal

---

*Completing a main idea chart*

Some of the main idea chart has been filled in. Fill in the rest of the chart with details from the first letter to the editor.

| What is the main idea? | | | |
|---|---|---|---|
| The after-school music program is important and fun. It should not be cancelled. | | | |

| What details help explain the main idea? | | | |
|---|---|---|---|
| Many students feel that the program should not be cancelled. | We learn how to play real instruments. | | |

Read a second letter to the editor.

1432 Evergreen Terrace
Shelbyville, Missouri  55555
December 18, 2001

Letters to the Editor
*The Shelbyville Gazette*
23 Highland Street
Shelbyville, Missouri  55555

Dear Editor:

Last Friday night, Ms. Romero's third-grade class presented a musical play. Our play was called "America: Land That I Love." It was a **tribute** to our country and a celebration of American music. We would like to thank everyone who helped us.

There are many teachers we would like to thank. We are grateful to Ms. Romero for picking a play that was so much fun to perform. Mr. Portland, the music teacher, helped us learn all our songs. Ms. Rothstein played the piano for practices and during the play. The art teacher, Mr. Ashmore, gave us great ideas for the costumes and sets. He is so talented and creative. Everyone said the costumes and sets were beautiful.

Many parents helped. We would like to thank them, as well. Our room parents, Mrs. Little and Mr. McKay, helped us learn our lines. They also arranged for the refreshments after the show. We'd like to thank the parents who brought the delicious cookies, cakes, and juice drinks.

We are grateful to the other members of our school community who helped us. The janitors helped set up for the play and helped clean up afterward. The librarian, Ms. Blanchard, made and copied our programs.

AMERICA: Land That I Love

Friday, December 14, 2001

Shelbyville School Auditorium

Finally, we would like to thank everyone who attended the musical. We had a lot of fun performing our play. We **appreciate** all the moms, dads, brothers, sisters, and grandparents who gave us lots of loud applause. Class plays are a lot of fun and a lot of hard work. Thanks to everyone who helped with ours!

Sincerely,
Ms. Romero's Third-Grade Class

---

*Using a main idea chart*

Use details from the second letter to the editor to fill in the main idea chart.

| What is the main idea? |
|---|
| |

| What details help explain the main idea? | | | |
|---|---|---|---|
| | | | |

## Check Your Understanding

Think about what you've read. Then answer these questions.

1. Joanna knows that if the music program is cancelled, it will
   - Ⓐ continue.
   - Ⓑ become popular.
   - Ⓒ end.
   - Ⓓ grow.

2. From the details in Joanna's letter, you can figure out that
   - Ⓐ she plays many instruments.
   - Ⓑ the trumpet is the first instrument she has played.
   - Ⓒ Mr. Portland can do many different magic tricks.
   - Ⓓ Joanna's parents do not like trumpet music.

3. Mr. Portland is a music instructor, which means that he
   - Ⓐ teaches music.
   - Ⓑ plays in a band.
   - Ⓒ writes music.
   - Ⓓ leads a band.

4. What is different about Joanna since she joined the music program?
   - Ⓐ She likes school more than she used to.
   - Ⓑ She no longer plays with children her own age.
   - Ⓒ She does not mind being in front of a crowd.
   - Ⓓ She gets along better with her parents.

5. The fourth paragraph of Joanna's letter is mainly about
   - Ⓐ why people should practice their music.
   - Ⓑ how hard Joanna has worked.
   - Ⓒ playing the trumpet in front of an audience.
   - Ⓓ how the music program has helped Joanna.

6. Joanna wrote her letter mainly to
   - Ⓐ get readers to support the after-school music program.
   - Ⓑ describe her regular music class.
   - Ⓒ entertain readers with a story about a musician.
   - Ⓓ explain how important it is to play a musical instrument.

7. The letter from the third-grade class is mostly about
   - Ⓐ a play about America.
   - Ⓑ thanking people who helped with the third-grade play.
   - Ⓒ how much fun it is to put on a musical play.
   - Ⓓ why it is important to take part in plays.

8. Which of these is a fact?
   - Ⓐ Ms. Rothstein played the piano for practices.
   - Ⓑ Mr. Ashmore gave us great ideas for costumes and sets.
   - Ⓒ Mr. Ashmore is so talented and creative.
   - Ⓓ Everyone said the costumes and sets were beautiful.

**9.** In the second letter, the best meaning for *refreshments* is

Ⓐ "parents and friends."

Ⓑ "play lines."

Ⓒ "members of the community."

Ⓓ "things to eat and drink."

**10.** Who helped the third graders by creating the programs?

Ⓐ the music teacher

Ⓑ the art teacher

Ⓒ the librarian

Ⓓ the room parents

**11.** The third graders show that they know what appreciate means by

Ⓐ putting on a play.

Ⓑ thanking people.

Ⓒ learning new songs.

Ⓓ working hard.

**12.** Whom do the third graders thank last in their letter?

Ⓐ Ms. Romero, their teacher

Ⓑ Mrs. Little and Mr. McKay, the room parents

Ⓒ the janitors

Ⓓ everyone who attended the play

## Extend Your Learning

- *Read an Article*

  With a partner, brainstorm a list of nonfiction topics. Then choose a topic and read an article about that topic in an encyclopedia or in a textbook. Take notes in a main idea chart as you read. Then use your filled-in chart to tell the main points of the article to a partner.

- *Write a Letter to the Editor*

  Write a letter to the editor of a children's magazine. You can write about an article that you read in the magazine, or about another topic that you think will interest readers. State your main idea clearly and include details that support the main idea. Use correct business letter form, as shown on page 8.

- *Present a Debate*

  Imagine that the principal of your school has just announced the cancellation of recess. Divide into teams of four. Half the teams should support the principal's decision. Half the teams should be against it. Work with your team to plan a speech about why you are for or against recess. Be sure that the speech has one main idea and details that support it. Take turns presenting your speeches.

# Recalling Facts and Details

## Learn About Recalling Facts and Details

*Thinking about the strategy*

When you read, look for **facts and details** that help you understand the main idea. Facts and details give information. They answer the questions *Who? What? When? Where? Why?* and *How?*

To find facts and details, first decide what the author is trying to say about a topic. That is the main idea. Then look for facts and details, such as names, dates, and events. Often, you will find these kinds of facts and details in descriptions, quotations, and lists.

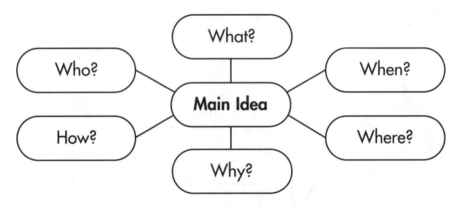

*Studying a model*

Read the passage and the notes beside it.

*The main idea is Amy's father built a playhouse.*

*Details tell about the friend and the swing set.*

*Details tell why Amy's father built a wood frame around the swing set.*

*Other details describe the finished playhouse.*

Last summer, a friend gave Amy's father an old swing set. Amy's father did not think that the swing set felt sturdy. He wanted to make it stronger.

Amy's father is a builder. He decided to build a wood frame to strengthen the swing set. The top part of the frame, above the swing set, was very strong. Amy's father decided to build a small playhouse on top of the frame. The wooden playhouse had two windows and a ladder on each end. Amy's father let Amy paint pictures on the inside walls.

# Learn About a Graphic Organizer

*Understanding a*
*facts and details web*

A **facts and details web** will help you keep track of facts and details in a selection. You can jot down notes in a facts and details web when you read articles, essays, and other nonfiction and fiction selections.

Here is a facts and details web for the passage on page 14. It shows the main idea of the passage and the facts and details that help explain the main idea.

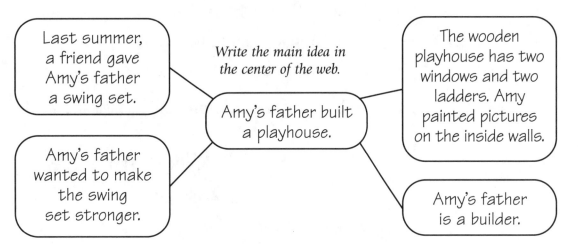

*On the outside
of the web,
write facts and
details that
help explain
the main idea.*

Last summer, a friend gave Amy's father a swing set.

*Write the main idea in
the center of the web.*

The wooden playhouse has two windows and two ladders. Amy painted pictures on the inside walls.

Amy's father built a playhouse.

Amy's father wanted to make the swing set stronger.

Amy's father is a builder.

When you fill in a facts and details web, you take notes about the names, dates, and events that help explain the main idea. This can make it easier for you to recall these facts and details later. Filling in a facts and detail web can help you prepare for a test, write a report, or explain the main idea of a selection.

*Why is Amy's playhouse on top of her swing set?*
Amy's father built a strong frame around the swing set and then decided to build a playhouse on top.

**As you read, ask yourself**

- What is the main idea of the paragraph, passage, or selection?
- What facts and details tell more about the main idea?

# Learn About a Form of Writing

*Focusing on a magazine article*

A **magazine article** gives information about a topic. Before an author writes a magazine article, the author figures out who will probably read the article. Then the author chooses facts and details that those readers will understand and enjoy.

A magazine article often has these features.

- It gives facts and details that tell about a topic.
- It has a catchy title. It may have headings for different parts.
- It often has photographs with captions.
- It may have sidebars, or separate sections, with extra facts.

Here is the opening paragraph from a magazine article.

> ## Arctic Brrrrrr!
>
> Nowhere is it darker or colder on Earth than it is in Antarctica during the winter. The dark lasts for six long months. The only light comes from the moon and the stars. The wind makes the freezing cold temperatures feel like 70 degrees below zero! The air often contains ice crystals that swirl and act like sharp tiny daggers.

*Organizing ideas in a facts and details web*

You can use a facts and details web to arrange facts and details in a magazine article. Here is a facts and details web for the paragraph above.

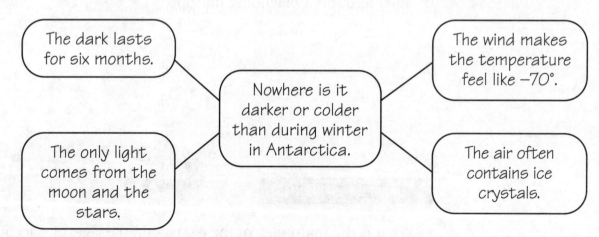

# Prepare for the Reading Selection

*Gaining knowledge*

You probably know that many kinds of birds migrate. Birds migrate, or move from one place to another, to find better weather and a good supply of food. The movement of birds from one place to another place is called migration. Many birds migrate great distances. Often, they return to the same place year after year. Scientists are not exactly sure how birds find their way back to the same place. They believe that the birds use specific sights, sounds, and smells along the route to find their way. In the selection you will read on the following pages, you will learn about the unusual habits of a group of birds that migrate every fall.

# Learn Vocabulary

*Understanding vocabulary*

The boxed words below are **boldfaced** in the selection. Learn the meaning of each word. Then write the word that answers the question.

| |
|---|
| overhead |
| cling |
| fumes |
| roost |
| computer |
| perch |

1. What word names a machine that can store and recall information? _____

2. Where would you look to see something in the sky?

   _____

3. When talking about birds, which two words mean "to sit" or "to rest"? _____  _____

4. What might you do to your parent's hand if you are afraid?

   _____

5. What word names unpleasant smokes or gases?

   _____

Read the first part of the magazine article "This School Is for the Birds" by Charles Schaeffer and Art Cosing. This article first appeared in the September 2001 on-line issue of *Ranger Rick*.

### This School Is for the Birds

Every September, the kids at Chapman School in Portland, Oregon, keep an eye on the sky while they're out on the playground. Why? They're waiting for some dark little birds to start circling above them. The birds are called Vaux's (VAWK-sez) swifts.

Thousands of them hang around the school in September. They fly in noisy circles **overhead**. Then, at sunset, the birds do an amazing thing. Whoosh—they dive into the school's tall chimney! It looks as if a huge vacuum cleaner just sucks them in.

The birds are usually safe from enemies when they sleep inside the chimney. And snuggling together helps keep them warm when autumn nights become cool. They **cling** to the chimney's walls and to each other with their sharp claws.

### Cold Classrooms

But wait a minute! Isn't it dangerous for birds to hang out in a chimney when the furnace is on? You bet! That's why the school's janitor always switched off the furnace when the birds arrived. "We don't want to roast the poor little birds or make them sick with smelly, smoky **fumes**," he'd say.

To keep warm in the cool school, the kids and teachers would wear sweaters, coats, hats, and mittens. They didn't mind—it was their way of helping the birds.

### Warm Again

This year things are going to be different. The kids and other bird lovers collected $75,000 so Chapman School could get another furnace. The new furnace has a chimney that birds can't fly into. The money was also used to fix up the old chimney. It won't be used for the furnace anymore, but it will be kept for the birds to stay in every September. And some of the money is being used to build a little nature center to tell the story of the swifts.

*These swifts make twittery and buzzy noises that sound something like tip-tip-tip-zeeeee-rip.*

---

*Completing a facts and details web*

Some of the facts and details web has been filled in. Add more facts and details that explain the main idea in the first part of the magazine article.

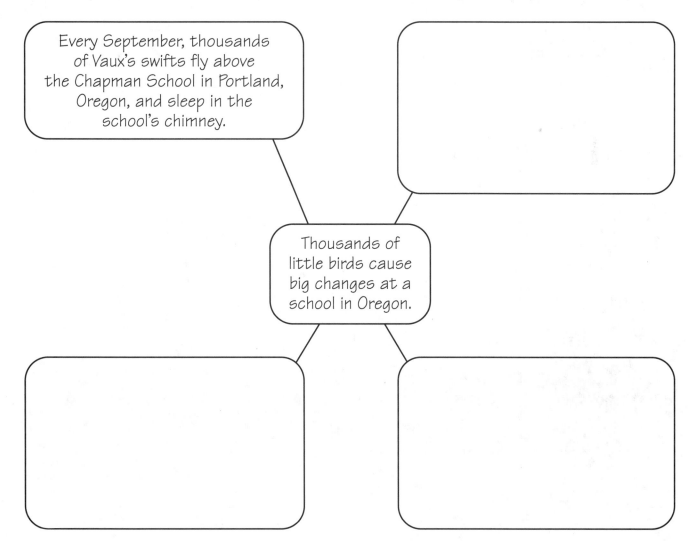

Every September, thousands of Vaux's swifts fly above the Chapman School in Portland, Oregon, and sleep in the school's chimney.

Thousands of little birds cause big changes at a school in Oregon.

Read the second part of the magazine article "This School Is for the Birds."

## What's the Story?

Millions of Vaux's swifts migrate down the West Coast every fall. On their way south, they stop at different places to rest and eat. They used to gather in old, dead trees to spend the night. But many of these trees have been cut down by people. So now, thousands of the swifts **roost** in chimneys instead.

The colony of swifts in and around Chapman School's chimney has grown to about 40,000 birds. That's the largest colony of Vaux's swifts in the world! Most of the swifts roost in the school's chimney, but some use other nearby chimneys or trees. Hundreds of people come to watch every evening when they fly into Chapman's chimney.

The swifts sleep in the chimney every night till the end of September. By October there are fewer and fewer insects flying around. Then most of the birds take off for the long trip south. As the kids wave good-bye to the birds, they hope that the swifts will always choose their chimney as the best place in the world to spend September!

*Fun Facts About Vaux's Swifts*

## Like Mice

Vaux's swifts are little brown-and-gray birds with long wings and short tails. A swift's body is less than five inches (13 cm) from beak to tail—about as long as a **computer** mouse.

## Why Bother Walking

These birds never walk or hop around on the ground. They can't even **perch** on a branch. During the day they fly, fly, fly. They eat while flying and take baths by skimming the surface of the water. They may even mate while flying. The only time they stop is to sit on their eggs or feed their babies.

## Whoosh!

These birds are swift flyers—they can speed along at 100 miles (160 km) per hour. And some fly as far as 2,500 miles (4,000 km) when migrating in spring and fall.

## Flight Food

Swifts eat almost nothing but flying insects. An adult swift eats thousands of them each day. And when nesting, each parent makes as many as 50 trips per day, delivering more than 5,000 insects to the babies.

*Using a facts and details web*

Fill in the facts and details web for the second part of the magazine article. This part describes the traits and habits of swifts.

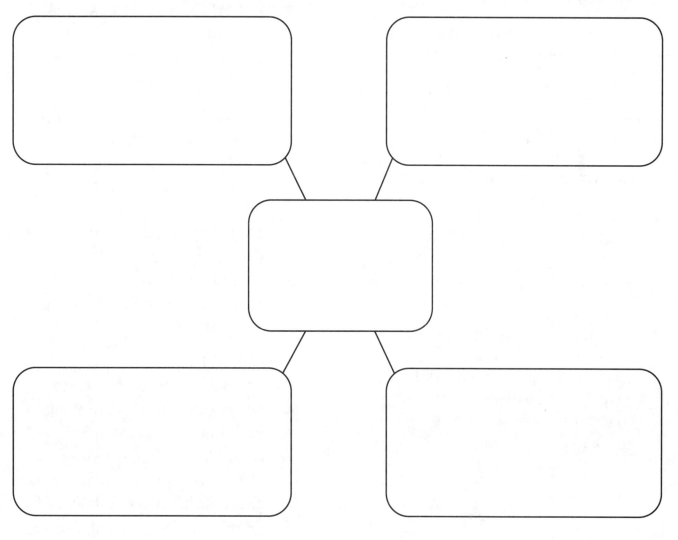

## Check Your Understanding

Think about what you've read. Then answer these questions.

1. Which of these events described in the article happens first?
   - Ⓐ The birds dive into the chimney.
   - Ⓑ The children wear coats in school.
   - Ⓒ The children keep an eye on the sky.
   - Ⓓ The birds fly in noisy circles.

2. When the birds cling, they
   - Ⓐ hold tightly to each other.
   - Ⓑ make noise.
   - Ⓒ dive quickly.
   - Ⓓ sharpen their claws.

3. In the past, why has the janitor turned off the Chapman School furnace in September?
   - Ⓐ The children got too warm.
   - Ⓑ Birds were in the chimney.
   - Ⓒ The furnace was broken.
   - Ⓓ The school needed to save money.

4. Which of these might you say about fumes?
   - Ⓐ "How pretty!"
   - Ⓑ "Stop that noise!"
   - Ⓒ "That's yummy."
   - Ⓓ "Something smells bad."

5. How much money did the children help raise for a new furnace?
   - Ⓐ $75,000
   - Ⓑ $40,000
   - Ⓒ $2,500
   - Ⓓ $5,000

6. What will happen now that the Chapman School has a new furnace?
   - Ⓐ The birds will fly into the new chimney.
   - Ⓑ The janitor will find a new job.
   - Ⓒ Children will not wear coats and mittens during school.
   - Ⓓ The birds will not have a warm, cozy place to sleep.

7. The section "What's the Story?" is mostly about
   - Ⓐ why birds migrate south in the fall.
   - Ⓑ why swifts live in large groups.
   - Ⓒ what kind of food swifts eat.
   - Ⓓ why swifts sleep in the school chimney in the fall.

8. What is special about the Vaux's swifts that sleep in the Chapman School chimney?
   - Ⓐ They are the only Vaux's swifts that roost in chimneys.
   - Ⓑ They are part of the world's largest colony of Vaux's swifts.
   - Ⓒ They do not migrate.
   - Ⓓ They eat more insects than other Vaux's swifts.

9. The authors included the section "Fun Facts About Vaux's Swifts" to
   - Ⓐ tell an entertaining story about birds that never sleep.
   - Ⓑ get readers to donate money to save swifts.
   - Ⓒ give more information about swifts.
   - Ⓓ describe how birds feed their babies.

**10.** When birds perch, they

   Ⓐ  sit and rest.

   Ⓑ  build a nest.

   Ⓒ  mate.

   Ⓓ  fly in circles.

**11.** A swift is about the same size as

   Ⓐ  a large insect.

   Ⓑ  a computer mouse.

   Ⓒ  an egg.

   Ⓓ  a rooster.

**12.** Which of these is an opinion?

   Ⓐ  Swifts eat while flying.

   Ⓑ  These birds are swift flyers.

   Ⓒ  They can fly at 100 miles per hour.

   Ⓓ  Vaux's swifts are little brown-and-gray birds.

## Extend Your Learning

• *Read a Magazine Article*

Skim different children's magazines. Look for an article with a catchy title that interests you. Then read the article. As you read, fill in a facts and details web to keep track of facts and details in the article. Then use the filled-in web to tell a partner the main ideas of the article.

• *Create a Bird Facts Booklet*

Work with a group to make a bird facts booklet. Do research at the library and on the Internet to find facts and details about birds. Take notes in a facts and details web, chart, or other graphic organizer. Then go over your notes together and decide how to arrange them in a small booklet of bird facts. Design and make a cover for your booklet. Place the bird booklet in the classroom or school library for others to read.

• *Present a Play*

Work with classmates to write a play based on the magazine article "This School Is for the Birds." Use the events described in the article. Then make up dialogue to go with these events. You might make stick puppets of the swifts for some children to hold up during the play. Practice and present your play to other classes in the school.

# Understanding Sequence

## Learn About Understanding Sequence

*Thinking about the strategy*

The order in which things happen in a story is called **sequence**. Authors use sequence to help readers understand how one event leads to another. The sequence of events in a story usually follows time order. Time order is the order in which events happen in time. You can often recognize sequence by looking for time order words such as *first, next,* and *last*.

Authors do not always use clue words to show sequence. Then you have to think about the order in which things happen.

**To understand sequence**

> **Ask:** What happens first? What happens next? What happens last?
>
> **Look** for clue words:
>
> | first | second | next | last |
> |-------|--------|------|------|
> | then | before | after | finally |
>
> **Think about** what happens before and after events in a story.

*Studying a model*

Read the story and the notes beside it.

*The time order words* before *and* after *are clues to sequence.*

*You can think about what happens after Mark shouts, "Fire, fire."*

*The words* later *and* finally *tell what happens after other events.*

Before he smelled the smoke, Mark heard his dog Rock barking. After Mark jumped out of bed, he shouted, "Fire, fire." Mark's parents and two sisters appeared at their bedroom doors. "Get down and crawl to the front door," Mark's dad said. "We'll meet by the lamppost." A few minutes later, Mark's family was safely out of the house. Mr. Jamison, the next-door neighbor, met them by the lamppost. "I've called the fire department," he said. Mark thought the fire trucks would never arrive, but finally, the scream of sirens filled the night.

# Learn About a Graphic Organizer

*Understanding a sequence chain*

A **sequence chain** will help you note the order of events in a selection. You can use a sequence chain to put events in order when you read stories, fables, fairy tales, and other fiction and nonfiction works.

Here is a sequence chain for the story on page 24. It shows the order in which the events happen in time.

*At the top of the sequence chain, list the event that happens first in time order.*

*In the next boxes, list what happens second, third, fourth, and so on.*

*At the bottom of the sequence chain, list the event that happens last in time order.*

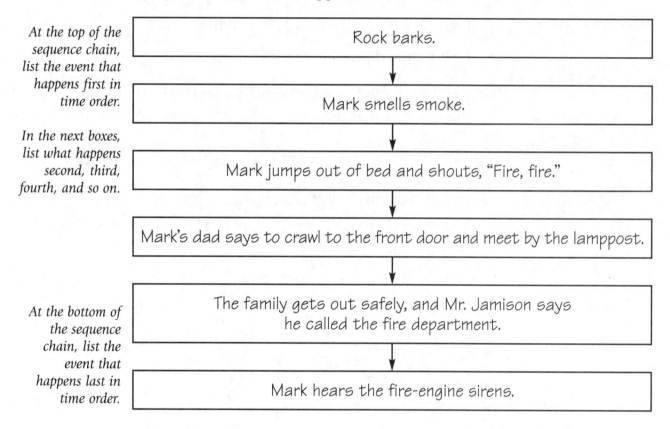

Rock barks.

↓

Mark smells smoke.

↓

Mark jumps out of bed and shouts, "Fire, fire."

↓

Mark's dad says to crawl to the front door and meet by the lamppost.

↓

The family gets out safely, and Mr. Jamison says he called the fire department.

↓

Mark hears the fire-engine sirens.

When you complete a sequence chain, you see clearly the order in which events happen in a story. You understand how events are connected. You see how one event leads to another.

*What happens because Rock barks?*
Mark realizes there is a fire. Mark warns his family, and everyone gets safely out of the house.

**As you read, ask yourself**

- What is the first thing that happens? What happens next?
- What clue words show sequence?
- What happens before and after events in a story?

# Learn About a Form of Writing

In a **realistic fiction story**, the setting, characters, and events are like places, people, and events in real life. Many realistic fiction stories take place in the present or in the recent past.

A realistic fiction story often has these features.

- It is often set in the present in a place that could be real.
- Its characters are like people in real life.
- It has events that could take place in real life.

Here is the opening passage from a realistic fiction story about baseball. Notice that the setting, characters, and events could be real.

> Jon stood on his porch and looked up at the sky. The sun was shining and not a cloud was in sight. He frowned. "No chance of rain," Jon said with a sigh. "Too bad."
>
> A moment later, Seth, who lived across the street, opened his front door and came running over to Jon.
>
> "I guess our wish for rain wasn't granted," Seth said. Both boys were quiet for a few minutes. Finally, Jon said, "We should get ready. We don't want to be late for the game."

You can use a sequence chain to keep track of the sequence of events in a realistic fiction story. Here is a filled-in sequence chain for the passage above.

| Jon sees that the sun is shining. He frowns and says, "Too bad." |
| --- |

↓

| Seth comes running over and says, "I guess our wish for rain wasn't granted." |
| --- |

↓

| Jon says, "We should get ready. We don't want to be late for the game." |
| --- |

# Prepare for the Reading Selection

*Gaining knowledge*

In the story you will read on the following pages, a young girl dreams of being in the circus. Perhaps, no way of life seems more thrilling and inviting to a youngster than circus life. Today, young people of all ages, from 3 to 19, can take classes in circus arts. Some actually perform in circuses that tour the country. Like adult circus performers, young circus performers walk the high wire, juggle, and do acrobatics, or tumbling tricks. Many enjoy being clowns and making audiences laugh. The life of a circus performer is fun and exciting, but it is also hard work. To learn the acts, young performers spend many hours, day after day, practicing. Many of them also spend weeks away from their family when the circus is on tour.

## Learn Vocabulary

*Understanding vocabulary*

The boxed words below are **boldfaced** in the selection. Learn the meaning of each word. Then write the word that completes the sentence.

| |
|---|
| apologize |
| rehearsal |
| applaud |
| regained |
| forbid |
| whisked |
| flourish |

1. The actors need more practice so they will have an extra

   _____.

2. School rules _____ us from running in the halls.

3. After a _____ of trumpets, the king and queen appeared.

4. If you're sorry for what you did, you should

   _____.

5. The wind _____ the leaves across the grass.

6. Put your hands together and _____ for our next guest.

7. He followed the doctors orders and soon

   _____ his health.

Read the first part of the realistic fiction story "A Birthday Surprise."

## A Birthday Surprise

Venus leaned over and threw a small stone into the hopscotch she had drawn on the sidewalk in front of Carrie's house. "Watch me," she hollered to her favorite babysitter. Carrie looked up from her book to watch Venus hop up and down the length of the hopscotch.

"Great job," Carrie called out to Venus.

"I didn't step on one single line or skip any blocks," Venus boasted. Just then a car pulled over and stopped. Carrie quickly got up from the lawn chair and walked over to Venus.

"Excuse me," the woman behind the wheel said. "Can you tell me how to get to the Stemper Building? I know it's on Main Street, but I've driven up and down Main Street at least five times. I still can't find the building."

Venus smiled brightly. "The Stemper Building is on the Main Street Extension," she said. "I know because my mom works there."

Carrie told the woman how to get to the Main Street Extension. As Carrie gave directions, Venus noticed that the woman was wearing a long raincoat over a beaded emerald green costume.

"Why are you dressed like that? You look like you're in the circus," Venus blurted out.

"Venus, that's rude," Carrie said. "**Apologize** this minute."

"That's okay," the woman said. " I am in the circus. I've just come from a dress **rehearsal**. I have an hour off and hope to see an old friend who works in the Stemper Building."

"Wow, I never met a real circus performer before," Venus said. "I wish I could be in the circus."

The woman smiled kindly. "Maybe someday you will be."

After the woman drove away, Venus started to daydream. She pictured herself in a shiny red costume, covered with sparkling beads. As she walked along the edge of the sidewalk, she pretended to be on a tightrope, high above a cheering crowd. Each time she slipped off the curb, she imagined she could hear the crowd gasp and then **applaud** wildly when she **regained** her balance.

Venus sighed. "How I would love to be in the circus, even for just one day," Venus said to Carrie.

"Why not make that your birthday wish," Carrie joked.

"Maybe I will," Venus said. She was only half-joking.

*Completing a sequence chain*

Think about what you have read so far. Then complete this sequence chain for the first part of the realistic fiction story.

| Venus is playing hopscotch in front of her babysitter Carrie's house. |
|---|

↓

| A woman drives up in a car and asks for directions to the Stemper Building. |
|---|

↓

| |
|---|

↓

| |
|---|

↓

| |
|---|

↓

| |
|---|

## Reading Selection—Part Two

Read the second part of the realistic fiction story "A Birthday Surprise."

The next evening, Venus's mother asked Venus to set an extra place for dinner. "My old friend Holly is in town," Venus's mother explained.

A few minutes later the doorbell rang. Venus opened the door.

"You're Mom's friend? You're Holly?" Venus asked in surprise.

Holly laughed. "And you're Sabrina's daughter! What a coincidence!"

Holly was the woman from the circus who had stopped to ask Venus for directions. Venus and Holly explained to Venus's parents how a chance event had brought Venus and Holly together. Then they all sat down for dinner. Holly, though, hardly had time to take a bite of food. Venus asked question after question about circus life. Finally, Venus's parents **forbid** her from asking any questions until dinner was done.

Later, as Holly was leaving, she handed Venus three tickets for the circus for Sunday afternoon. "Wow!" Venus said. "Sunday's my birthday. Thanks!" The tickets were for front row seats.

Sunday finally came. Venus enjoyed every minute of the circus. She clapped loudest, however, for Holly, who did tricks on the back of a beautiful white horse.

Then, toward the end of the show, the ringmaster stepped into the spotlight. "Before the Grand Finale Parade begins," he said, "we want to welcome a special guest. Her name is Venus Thompson. Today is Venus's ninth birthday, and she has a special birthday wish."

Venus couldn't believe her ears or her eyes. One minute she was sitting in her seat watching the show. The next minute, Holly had **whisked** her away to a dressing room. Holly handed Venus a sparkling red costume. "I must be dreaming," Venus said as she put on the beautiful costume.

Next, Venus heard a **flourish** of music. "Follow me," Holly said. "Do as I tell you. And don't forget to smile." Venus followed Holly. With Holly's help, Venus climbed onto the back of Holly's horse. Holly climbed up behind her.

The Grand Finale Parade began. Venus squeezed her eyes shut. "This *has* to be a dream," she said. She opened her eyes. She was still dressed in the sparkling red costume. She was still sitting high up on a white horse with Holly behind her.

The parade of performers and animals circled the center ring. Venus looked out into the crowd. She saw people clapping and cheering. She saw her parents smiling and waving. "I'm in the circus!" she thought. "My wish has come true!" That's when she remembered to smile. It was the biggest smile that Venus had ever smiled in her whole nine years.

*Using a
sequence chain*

Fill in the sequence chain for the second part of the realistic fiction story.

```
┌─────────────────────────────────────────────┐
│                                             │
│                                             │
│                                             │
└─────────────────────────────────────────────┘
                      │
                      ▼
┌─────────────────────────────────────────────┐
│                                             │
│                                             │
│                                             │
└─────────────────────────────────────────────┘
                      │
                      ▼
┌─────────────────────────────────────────────┐
│                                             │
│                                             │
│                                             │
└─────────────────────────────────────────────┘
                      │
                      ▼
┌─────────────────────────────────────────────┐
│                                             │
│                                             │
└─────────────────────────────────────────────┘
                      │
                      ▼
┌─────────────────────────────────────────────┐
│                                             │
│                                             │
└─────────────────────────────────────────────┘
```

## Check Your Understanding

Think about what you've read. Then answer these questions.

1.  What is Venus doing when she meets Holly for the first time?
    - Ⓐ  riding a white horse
    - Ⓑ  pretending to be in the circus
    - Ⓒ  playing hopscotch
    - Ⓓ  reading a book

2.  Why can't Holly find the Stemper Building?
    - Ⓐ  She doesn't know where Main Street is.
    - Ⓑ  She gets lost easily.
    - Ⓒ  The building has a new name.
    - Ⓓ  She has the wrong address.

3.  The words *blurted out* mean that Venus
    - Ⓐ  "spoke without thinking."
    - Ⓑ  "laughed out loud."
    - Ⓒ  "got dizzy."
    - Ⓓ  "forgot everything."

4.  Carrie told Venus to apologize. She wanted Venus to
    - Ⓐ  play a game.
    - Ⓑ  say she was sorry.
    - Ⓒ  go away.
    - Ⓓ  stop talking.

5.  What happens right after Holly drives away?
    - Ⓐ  Venus draws a hopscotch.
    - Ⓑ  Venus puts on a shiny red costume.
    - Ⓒ  Venus makes a birthday wish.
    - Ⓓ  Venus daydreams about being in the circus.

6.  People applaud when they
    - Ⓐ  are sad.
    - Ⓑ  have a problem.
    - Ⓒ  enjoy a show.
    - Ⓓ  sleep late.

7.  From the story, you can figure out that Venus's mom and Holly
    - Ⓐ  see each other only once a year.
    - Ⓑ  have known each other for a long time.
    - Ⓒ  joined the circus together.
    - Ⓓ  went to the same college.

8.  In Part Two, which of these gives a clue to the meaning of *coincidence*?
    - Ⓐ  directions
    - Ⓑ  hardly had time
    - Ⓒ  bite of food
    - Ⓓ  chance event

9.  When Holly whisked Venus away, Holly
    - Ⓐ  quickly took Venus away.
    - Ⓑ  pushed Venus out of the way.
    - Ⓒ  wished Venus would go away.
    - Ⓓ  twirled Venus around.

10. Which of these events happens last in the story?
    - Ⓐ  Venus questions Holly about circus life.
    - Ⓑ  Holly gives Venus circus tickets.
    - Ⓒ  Venus takes part in a circus parade.
    - Ⓓ  Venus watches Holly do tricks on the back of a horse.

**11.** Which of these tells what the story is mostly about?

Ⓐ A young girl makes a birthday wish about being in the circus.

Ⓑ A young girl and a circus performer become friends.

Ⓒ A circus performer gets lost and happens to meet the daughter of an old friend.

Ⓓ A girl's birthday wish comes true when her mother's friend invites her to be in the circus.

**12.** The author wrote the story mainly to

Ⓐ persuade readers to join the circus.

Ⓑ entertain readers with a story about a girl named Venus.

Ⓒ describe circus costumes.

Ⓓ explain how to play sidewalk games like hopscotch.

## Extend Your Learning

- *Read a Realistic Fiction Story*

  Read another realistic fiction story. You may read a new story, or you may reread a story you have read before. As you read, fill in a sequence chain to keep track of the order in which important story events happen. Then use your completed sequence chain to retell the story to a partner.

- *Write a Thank-you Letter*

  Imagine that you are Venus. Write a thank-you letter to Holly for arranging for you to be in the circus. Explain how this made you feel and why it was so special to you. Include details from the story in your letter. You can look over your filled-in sequence chains on pages 29 and 31 of the lesson to recall story events. Share your letter with the class.

- *Continue the Story*

  Work with a group to write a new ending for "A Birthday Surprise," or continue one of the stories started on page 24 or page 26. Fill in a sequence chain as you decide the order in which important story events will happen. Then use the filled-in sequence chain to write a story ending. Share your story with other groups.

# Recognizing Cause and Effect

## Learn About Recognizing Cause and Effect

*Thinking about the strategy*

A **cause** is an event that makes something happen. An **effect** is what happens because of another event. When you read a story, you can look for events that are causes and events that are effects. You can often recognize a cause or an effect by looking for clue words such as *because, so,* and *as a result.*

Authors do not always use clue words to show causes and effects. Then you have to think about what happens and why it happens.

| **To recognize causes and effects** | **Ask:** What happened? *(to find an effect)* <br> **Ask:** Why did it happen? *(to find a cause)* <br> **Look** for clue words: <br>    so       because      reason <br>    since      if           as a result <br> **Think about** what you already know about how one thing causes another thing to happen in real life. |

*Studying a model*

Read the paragraph and the notes beside it.

*The clue word because signals a cause.*

*The clue words as a result signal an effect.*

*Another effect is that other gardeners ask for advice.*

*You can figure out that many people read the neighborhood newsletter.*

Because Mrs. Como enjoys gardening, she spends many hours a week outdoors, planting, weeding, and watering. As a result of all her hard work, Mrs. Como has the most beautiful flower gardens in our neighborhood. Her plants are so healthy and strong that neighbors are always asking her for advice. My mother writes and publishes a town newsletter. She asked Mrs. Como to write a gardening column for the newsletter. Mrs. Como agreed. Now people in the whole town can learn her secrets.

# Learn About a Graphic Organizer

*Understanding a cause-and-effect diagram*

A **cause-and-effect diagram** will help you identify a cause-and-effect relationship. A cause-and-effect diagram can also help you see the connection between events in a story. You can use a cause-and-effect diagram when you read fiction and nonfiction selections.

Here is a cause-and-effect diagram for the paragraph on page 34. It shows how events in the paragraph are connected.

| CAUSE | EFFECT |
|---|---|

*In each Cause box, list an event that is the reason something happens.*

| Mrs. Como enjoys gardening. | → | She spends hours planting, weeding, and watering. |
|---|---|---|

*In each Effect box, list an event that is the result of something that happens.*

| Mrs. Como works hard in her gardens. | → | She has the most beautiful gardens in the neighborhood. |
|---|---|---|

| Her plants are healthy and strong. | → | Neighbors ask for advice. |
|---|---|---|

| She writes a gardening column. | → | People in the whole town can learn her gardening secrets. |
|---|---|---|

When you complete a cause-and-effect diagram, you see connections between events in a story. You understand why things happen.

*Why do so many people in the neighborhood want to know Mrs. Como's gardening secrets?*
Mrs. Como has the most beautiful gardens in the neighborhood.

**As you read, ask yourself**

- What happened? Why did it happen?
- What clue words show causes and effects?
- What do I already know in real life about how things cause other things to happen?

# Learn About a Form of Writing

*Focusing on an informational story*

An **informational story** is a kind of story that teaches about a topic while it tells a story. Like other stories, an informational story has characters, a setting, and a problem for the main character to solve.

An informational story often has these features.

- It usually has real-life characters and events.
- The purpose of the story is to give information about a topic.
- The characters often give facts and details about the topic.

Here is a paragraph from an informational story about a girl on a trip to a national park. Notice the details about the park.

> The travel agent had said that it was impossible to get around Mesa Verde National Park without a car. So after their plane landed in Durango, Colorado, Janie's dad rented a van. Since Mesa Verde is less than 40 miles west of Durango, they arrived at the park's Far View Lodge less than an hour later. Janie's room wasn't fancy. There wasn't even a telephone. Yet she didn't mind. Far View sits on a high point in Mesa Verde. From the window, she could see into three states!

*Organizing ideas in a cause-and-effect diagram*

You can use a cause-and-effect diagram to identify causes and effects in an informational story. Here is a filled-in cause-and-effect diagram for the paragraph above.

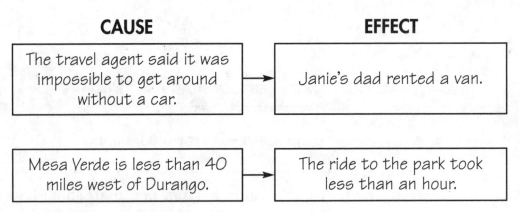

| CAUSE | EFFECT |
|-------|--------|
| The travel agent said it was impossible to get around without a car. | Janie's dad rented a van. |
| Mesa Verde is less than 40 miles west of Durango. | The ride to the park took less than an hour. |

# Prepare for the Reading Selection

*Gaining knowledge* The informational story you will read on the following pages is about a right whale. Right whales got their name hundreds of years ago. Then people who hunted for whales said that these whales were the "right" whales to kill. The whales were so full of blubber, or fat, that the whales floated even after they were dead. This made it easy for the hunters to pull a dead whale back to shore. Today right whales are endangered. That means that there are so few of them that they are in danger of becoming extinct. There are only about 300 right whales left in the world. These whales are protected by law. However, human activities, such as fishing and boating, continue to threaten their lives. When a right whale is hurt, ocean scientists try everything they can to save it.

## Learn Vocabulary

*Understanding vocabulary*

The boxed words below are **boldfaced** in the selection. Learn the meaning of each word. Then write the word beside its definition.

| |
|---|
| advice |
| injured |
| plight |
| infection |
| injected |
| sedative |
| volume |

1. a sore that can make someone sick _____

2. words meant to help another person _____

3. loudness _____

4. hurt or wounded _____

5. stuck with a needle filled with medicine

   _____

6. a difficult condition or problem _____

7. a kind of medicine that helps calm people or animals

   _____

Read the first part of the informational story "A Happy Ending."

## A Happy Ending

Trey sat on the den floor with his legs crossed and a piece of poster board in front of him. He was frowning. "It's no use," he said aloud. "I can't think of a good idea for my poster."

Mrs. Inez, Trey's mom, put down the book she was reading. "Can I help?" she asked.

"I have to think of a good idea for a poster that tells a true story about nature," he said. "But I can't think of anything."

"Maybe you're trying too hard," Mrs. Inez said. "Sometimes when you stop trying to think of an idea, an idea will just come to you as if from nowhere."

Trey was not sure how an idea could come from nowhere. However, since he couldn't think of anything at all, he decided to take his mom's **advice**. "Okay, I won't think about the poster for a while. Is it all right if I watch television?" he asked.

"Sure," his mom answered. "Let's find something to watch together."

Trey picked up the remote and started flipping through the channels.

"Is that about the **injured** whale?" his mother asked when the image of a whale filled the television screen.

Trey and his mom had followed the **plight** of the whale all summer. Trey knew that the whale was an endangered right whale. Somehow, a piece of green fishing line had become entangled, or stuck, in the whale's jaw. The line had caused an **infection** that made the whale ill. As a result, the once shiny black whale had turned a sickly pale gray.

Trey also knew that scientists at the Ocean Institute had tried at least four times to rescue the whale. The first time, they **injected** the whale with a **sedative**. The plan was to slow the whale down enough so that a rescue team could get close enough to remove the fishing line. The sedative did slow the whale, but not for long. The drugs wore off quickly. The rescuers did not have enough time to help the whale.

Scientists tried the same plan a week later. This time they used a stronger drug. Then they tried to tie leather straps to the whale's tail. The plan was to tug the whale backwards. Rescuers would then pull the rope from its mouth. The plan failed. The giant whale was too active. The team could not get close enough to attach the straps. Rescuers were very disappointed.

---

*Completing a cause-and-effect diagram*
Think about what you have read so far. Then complete the cause-and-effect diagram for the first part of the informational story.

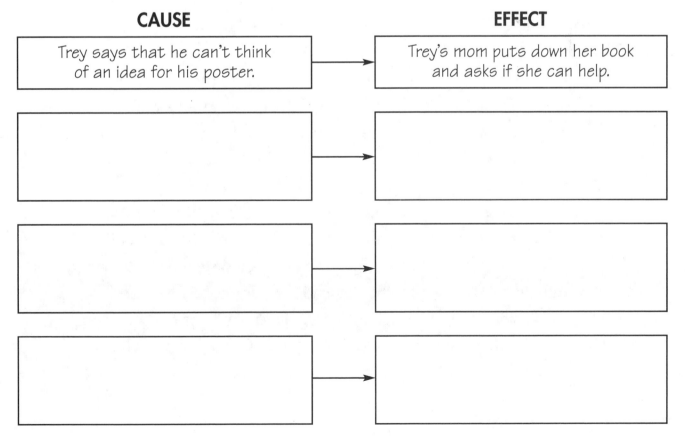

| CAUSE | EFFECT |
|---|---|
| Trey says that he can't think of an idea for his poster. | Trey's mom puts down her book and asks if she can help. |
| | |
| | |
| | |

Read the second part of the informational story "A Happy Ending."

Throughout the summer, television and newspaper reporters had told about the whale's struggle. As a result, people all over the country knew about Oliver. That's the nickname someone gave the sick whale. Everyone wanted to help Oliver. Some people had even written to the Ocean Institute to suggest ways to save Oliver. Scientists did not use any of these ideas. However, they said they would if an idea made sense and none of their ideas worked.

Oliver was one of only 300 right whales alive in the whole world. Right whales, which weigh about 50 tons, often get tangled in fishing lines because of how they feed. 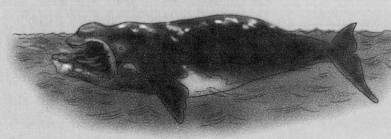 They eat with their mouths wide open. They skim just below the surface of the water. Whatever is in the water goes right in. The whales get tangled in fishing nets and lines without knowing it.

Once a whale is entangled, the whale can have trouble eating and swimming. Over time, a rope or fishing line can work its way into a whale's jaw. This can cause deep wounds that get infected and leave scars. Scientists think that many right whales have died as a result of becoming entangled.

Now Trey turned up the television **volume** so that he and his mother could hear the latest news on Oliver. The newscaster said, "Fog and heavy rain along the Canadian coast made it impossible for helicopters to track Oliver today. As many of you know, Oliver swam from the New England coast to Canada at the end of July. According to Dr. Ames of the Ocean Institute, most right whales swim north to Canada around that time of year. They go there to feed.

"Once Oliver reached the Bay of Fundy, a rescue team made one more attempt to free the whale from the fishing line. We are happy to report they were successful. Since then, Oliver has been getting healthier and healthier. Right whales can live for sixty years. Let's hope that Oliver, who is about eighteen years old, gets to enjoy many more birthdays."

At the end of the report, Trey turned off the television. An idea was forming in his head. "Mom," he said. "Can I look for some information on the Internet before bed?"

"Sure," Mrs. Inez said.

Trey was up early the next morning even though it was Saturday. He dressed, ate breakfast, and quickly went to work on his poster. He worked all morning and afternoon. When he was finished, he brought it downstairs to show his mom.

"You were right, Mom," he said smiling. "I stopped trying to think of an idea, and an idea came to me." He showed his mom his poster. It told the story of a whale named Oliver. The title was "A Happy Ending."

---

*Using a cause-and-effect diagram*

Fill in the cause-and-effect diagram for the second part of the informational story.

| CAUSE | EFFECT |
|-------|--------|
|       |        |
|       |        |
|       |        |
|       |        |

## Check Your Understanding

Think about what you've read. Then answer these questions.

1. What does Trey's poster have to show?
   - Ⓐ how to save a whale
   - Ⓑ a true story about nature
   - Ⓒ an event from Trey's life
   - Ⓓ what Trey did during summer vacation

2. Trey takes his mom's advice. He
   - Ⓐ does what she suggests.
   - Ⓑ picks up her book.
   - Ⓒ holds her hand.
   - Ⓓ turns away from her.

3. You can figure out that Trey decides to watch television
   - Ⓐ to learn about whales.
   - Ⓑ because he feels sick.
   - Ⓒ because he is bored and has nothing else to do.
   - Ⓓ to take his mind off his poster.

4. If a whale is injured, it is
   - Ⓐ small.
   - Ⓑ hurt.
   - Ⓒ happy.
   - Ⓓ alone.

5. Why had the right whale turned from black to gray?
   - Ⓐ Right whales turn gray as they get older.
   - Ⓑ There was no reason.
   - Ⓒ The fishing line had caused an infection that made the whale sick.
   - Ⓓ Scientists injected it with a drug.

6. Which of these statements is an opinion?
   - Ⓐ Scientists tried four times to rescue the whale.
   - Ⓑ The sedative did slow the whale.
   - Ⓒ The plan failed.
   - Ⓓ Rescuers were very disappointed.

7. Which of these is not an effect of a whale becoming entangled?
   - Ⓐ It can have trouble swimming.
   - Ⓑ It can have trouble eating.
   - Ⓒ It can skim the water.
   - Ⓓ It can become scarred.

8. When you turn down the volume on a television set, you change the
   - Ⓐ color.
   - Ⓑ sound.
   - Ⓒ station choice.
   - Ⓓ power on or off.

9. Which of these events happens last in the informational story?
   - Ⓐ Oliver swims to Canada.
   - Ⓑ A fishing line gets tangled in Oliver's jaw.
   - Ⓒ Someone nicknames the whale Oliver.
   - Ⓓ Scientists try to attach leather straps to Oliver's tail.

10. What is different about Trey at the end of the story than from the beginning of the story?
    - Ⓐ He is smiling.
    - Ⓑ He is worried.
    - Ⓒ He is sad.
    - Ⓓ He is tired.

**11.** From the information in the story, you can predict that

Ⓐ Trey will get the best grade in his class for his poster.

Ⓑ scientists will never try to help a tangled whale again.

Ⓒ whales will stop getting tangled.

Ⓓ Oliver will probably not die from his wound.

**12.** The author told this story mainly to

Ⓐ describe how whales eat.

Ⓑ give information about right whales.

Ⓒ tell an enjoyable story about a boy and his pet whale.

Ⓓ persuade people to stop fishing.

## Extend Your Learning

- *Write a Fiction Story*

  What do you think happens to Oliver after the story ends? Brainstorm ideas for a story about Oliver, the whale. Decide where your story will take place and what other characters will be in the story. You may want to make Trey a character in your story. Perhaps, Trey and Oliver become friends and have an exciting adventure at sea. Use your imagination as you plan and write your story. Then share your story with a group.

- *Read an Article About Whales*

  With a partner, find and read a nonfiction article about whales. As you read, fill in a cause-and-effect diagram that shows how details and events are connected. Then use your diagram to explain to the class what you learned about whales.

- *Create a Nature Strip*

  Make a comic strip that tells a story about nature. For example, you might show how a flower blooms, how clouds form, or how bees make honey. Do research to learn as many facts and details as you can about your topic. You can take notes in a cause-and-effect diagram or another kind of graphic organizer. Then use your notes to create your nature strip.

# Comparing and Contrasting

## Learn About Comparing and Contrasting

*Thinking about the strategy*

When you **compare**, you think about how things are alike. For example, basketball and soccer are the same in some ways. Both are played with a ball. In both, the players form teams. Both are fast games. You can probably think of other similarities.

When you **contrast**, you think about how things are different. For example, basketball and soccer are unlike in some ways. Basketball players use their hands, but soccer players don't. A basketball is bigger than a soccer ball. You can probably think of other differences between the games.

As you read, notice what authors are comparing and contrasting. You may find clue words that help you compare. Here are a few:

*alike      same      both      similarities*

You may find clue words that help you contrast. Here are a few:

*different      unlike      but      however      differences*

Words with the endings *-er* and *-est* also point out differences.

As you read, use compare/contrast clue words to think about what is alike and different about the topics.

---

*Studying a model*

Read the paragraph and the notes beside it.

*Leopards and jaguars are being compared and contrasted.*

Picture two wild cats. They are both large, fierce hunters. Both have spotted coats. These cats look alike, but they are different animals. One is a leopard. The other is a jaguar. Jaguars have heavier bodies than leopards, with bigger heads and jaws. Leopards live in Africa and Asia. Jaguars live in Central and South America. Jaguars and leopards have both been hunted for their skins. They are very rare animals in the wild.

# Learn About a Graphic Organizer

*Understanding a Venn diagram*

A **Venn diagram** is a kind of drawing that shows how things are alike and different. You can use a Venn diagram when you want to compare and contrast people, animals, places, and things in fiction and nonfiction selections.

Here is a filled-in Venn diagram for the paragraph on page 44.

*Use this part to show how a leopard is different from a jaguar.*

*Use this part to show how a jaguar is different from a leopard.*

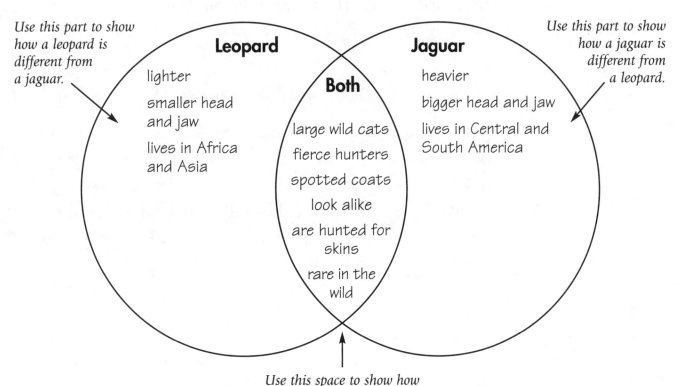

**Leopard**

lighter

smaller head and jaw

lives in Africa and Asia

**Both**

large wild cats

fierce hunters

spotted coats

look alike

are hunted for skins

rare in the wild

**Jaguar**

heavier

bigger head and jaw

lives in Central and South America

*Use this space to show how a leopard and a jaguar are alike.*

A Venn diagram helps you see how two things are alike and different.

*How are leopards and jaguars different?*
A leopard has a lighter body, and a smaller head and jaw, than a jaguar. Leopards live in Africa and Asia, while jaguars live in Central and South America.

**As you read, ask yourself**

- What are the two topics?
- How are they alike? How are they different?
- What do compare/contrast clue words tell me?

45

*Focusing on a fable*

A **fable** is a short made-up story that teaches a lesson.

A fable often has these special features.

- It has animals that talk and behave like people.
- It teaches an important lesson in an entertaining way.
- Sometimes the lesson is stated at the end of the story.

Here is a well-known fable.

> ## The Tortoise and the Hare
>
> The tortoise and the hare agree to run a race. They are both sure of themselves. Tortoise is sure that if he keeps going, he can finish the race. Hare is too sure of himself, however. He decides to take a nap before he reaches the finish line. Tortoise is slow and steady. Hare may be faster, but he is not steady. At the end, Tortoise wins and Hare loses.

*Organizing ideas in a Venn diagram*

Here is a filled-in Venn diagram for the fable above. It helps you compare and contrast the characters in the fable.

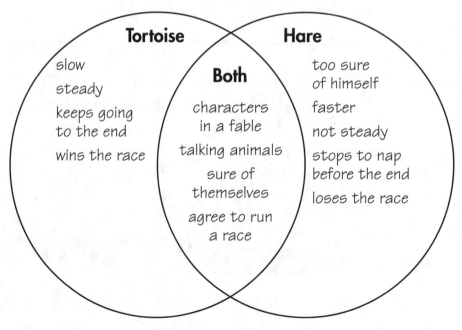

**Tortoise**
slow
steady
keeps going to the end
wins the race

**Both**
characters in a fable
talking animals
sure of themselves
agree to run a race

**Hare**
too sure of himself
faster
not steady
stops to nap before the end
loses the race

# Prepare for the Reading Selections

*Gaining knowledge*

On the pages that follow, you will read two fables. They are usually found in collections of fables by Aesop (EE-sop). Aesop was a storyteller who lived in Greece more than 2,500 years ago. Not much is known about Aesop, though he may have been a slave who had been freed. Aesop's fables were collected and written down after he died. They spread throughout the world and are still being retold today.

As you read the fables, think about comparing and contrasting. Ask yourself how characters are alike and different. Ask yourself how the fables are alike and different, too.

## Learn Vocabulary

*Understanding vocabulary*

The boxed words below are **boldfaced** in the selections. Learn the meaning of each word. Then write the word that matches the clue.

| |
|---|
| mercy |
| pleas |
| gnawed |
| heartily |
| generosity |

1. Another word for *bitten* _____

2. Opposite of *selfishness* _____

3. "Help! Save me!" for example _____

4. A show of kindness _____

5. How a hungry person eats _____

Read the fable "The Lion and the Mouse."

### The Lion and the Mouse

One afternoon, Lion slept in the shade of a large rock. Mouse, scampering above, slipped and fell right on the beast's nose. Lion awoke with a roar. He clapped his paw over Mouse. Then Lion opened his huge jaws and dangled Mouse in front of his teeth.

"Please, Lion, please don't eat me!" squeaked Mouse. "Have **mercy**, oh, great Lion. I am so small, and you are so large. I could not possibly satisfy your hunger."

Lion shook his head with wonder at the fast-talking creature.

Mouse continued. "I am much weaker than you. You are so strong. I am too easy a catch for a mighty hunter such as yourself. Please have mercy!"

Lion was amused by Mouse's **pleas**. "Off with you, then!" said Lion, gently releasing the tiny creature.

"Someday, you too may find yourself in danger," said Mouse. "Then I will repay you for your kindness."

Lion just chuckled. "What a ridiculous idea," he thought as he drifted back to sleep.

Not long afterward, Lion was wandering through the woods when he stepped into a hole. It was a trap placed there by hunters. A large net dropped on top of Lion. He struggled to break free of it, but the net just wrapped itself more tightly around him.

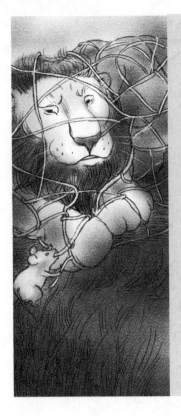

Lion roared with rage. He roared with helplessness. He roared loudly enough to shake the leaves on trees. Off in the distance, Mouse heard the roars. He recognized Lion's voice.

Soon Mouse appeared beside the net. "Quiet down," he said to Lion. "I will help you." Mouse set to work on the cords that bound Lion.

Mouse **gnawed** and nibbled. One cord snapped. He nibbled and gnawed. Another cord snapped. The opening grew larger and larger as Mouse worked. At last, Lion broke out of the net. He leaped from the hole.

"I told you I would help you," said Mouse.

"Thank you," Lion answered gratefully.

*No kindness is ever wasted.*

---

*Completing a Venn diagram*

The Venn diagram below has been partly filled in. Add more likenesses and differences from the fable.

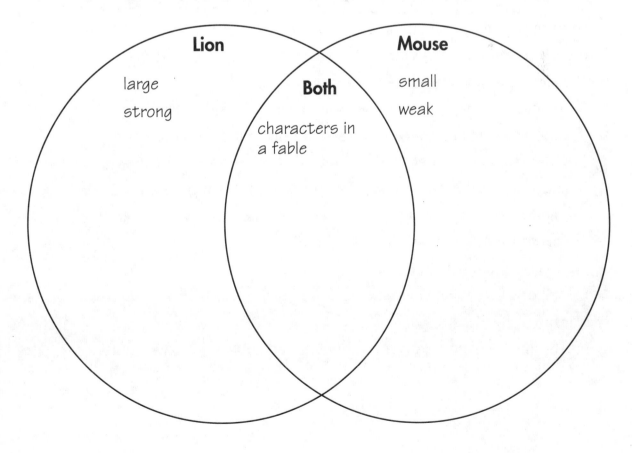

**Lion**

large
strong

**Both**

characters in a fable

**Mouse**

small
weak

Read the fable "The Fox and the Stork."

### The Fox and the Stork

Fox was in a playful mood. He felt the need for a good joke.
When he saw Stork in the neighborhood, he waved hello.

"Greetings, my good friend," Fox said to Stork. "I would enjoy your
company this evening. Would you like to have dinner at my house?"

"Thank you for inviting me," said Stork. "I would love to share a meal with you."

That evening, Fox carried a dish to the table. It was a dish so shallow that
it was nearly flat. It held soup. Fox began lapping up the soup greedily.
"It's delicious. Help yourself!" he said to Stork.

Of course, Stork's mouth was different from Fox's. Her bill was too long
and narrow for the flat dish. She could not get a drop of soup.

"Please, have some!" encouraged Fox. "You're hardly eating a thing."

Stork said nothing until Fox had finished the soup. Then she said, "Please
do me the honor of visiting me tomorrow evening. I would like to return
the favor by having you dine with me."

"I'd be delighted to come," replied Fox.

"Please remember to come very hungry," said Stork. "There will be plenty
of food."

The next evening, Fox arrived. "I'm very hungry," he told Stork.

"Good. The food is ready," said Stork, pointing to a large container on the floor. It was a tall vase with a narrow neck. Stork had no trouble reaching in with her long bill. She ate **heartily**. Fox, however, couldn't get his wide nose into the vase. He could not get even a morsel to his mouth.

Fox's belly rumbled, but he did not complain. After all, how could he find fault with Stork when she was merely repaying his **generosity**?

*Using a Venn diagram*    Fill in this Venn diagram with information from the fable.

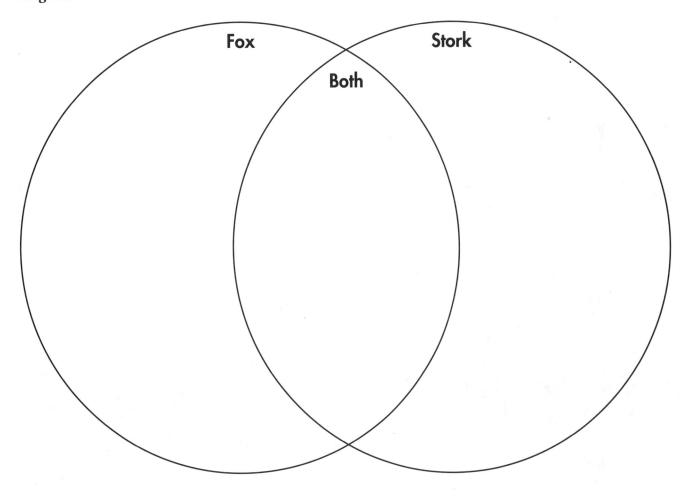

## Check Your Understanding

Think about what you've read. Then answer these questions.

1. How is Lion in "The Lion and the Mouse" like Fox in "The Fox and the Stork"?
   - Ⓐ Both are tricky animals.
   - Ⓑ Both learn a lesson.
   - Ⓒ Both catch a weaker animal.
   - Ⓓ Both are hungry.

2. How does Lion show mercy?
   - Ⓐ He dangles Mouse in front of his teeth.
   - Ⓑ He awakens with a roar.
   - Ⓒ He chuckles at the thought of Mouse helping him.
   - Ⓓ He lets Mouse go.

3. Why did Lion roar with helplessness?
   - Ⓐ He was caught and couldn't get free.
   - Ⓑ Mouse had landed on his nose and awakened him.
   - Ⓒ He wanted Mouse to hear him.
   - Ⓓ He was showing how grateful he felt.

4. What does Mouse do when he hears the roars of trapped Lion?
   - Ⓐ runs to help Lion
   - Ⓑ climbs a tree
   - Ⓒ gnaws on the net
   - Ⓓ begs for mercy

5. Mouse makes pleas when he
   - Ⓐ vows to repay Lion.
   - Ⓑ nibbles on the net.
   - Ⓒ tells Lion to "Quiet down."
   - Ⓓ begs Lion to let him go.

6. In the fable, how are Lion and Mouse alike?
   - Ⓐ They are both mighty hunters.
   - Ⓑ They both help the other out of danger.
   - Ⓒ They both beg for mercy.
   - Ⓓ They both get caught in a net.

7. At the start, Stork says to Fox, "Thank you for inviting me." What is Stork probably thinking?
   - Ⓐ "Fox may want to trick me."
   - Ⓑ "That's very nice of Fox."
   - Ⓒ "I hope that Fox does not serve food in a flat dish."
   - Ⓓ "Fox is not really my friend."

8. Stork eats heartily, which means
   - Ⓐ while laughing.
   - Ⓑ with tiny bites.
   - Ⓒ with pleasure.
   - Ⓓ loudly.

9. Fox "could not get even a morsel to his mouth." What is a morsel?
   - Ⓐ a bit of food
   - Ⓑ a fork or spoon
   - Ⓒ the rim of a tall vase
   - Ⓓ the tip of the tongue

10. What lesson does "The Fox and the Stork" teach?
   - Ⓐ Look before you leap.
   - Ⓑ Two wrongs do not make a right.
   - Ⓒ You are known by the company you keep.
   - Ⓓ A trickster may be tricked himself.

**11.** Which of these could happen in real life?

   Ⓐ  A lion sleeps in the shade of a large rock.

   Ⓑ  A lion chuckles.

   Ⓒ  A fox waves to a stork.

   Ⓓ  A stork invites a fox to dinner.

**12.** The author wrote these fables

   Ⓐ  to explain and inform.

   Ⓑ  to persuade listeners to take action.

   Ⓒ  to entertain and to teach lessons.

   Ⓓ  to describe how animals act.

## Extend Your Learning

- *Take a Point of View*

  Take the point of view of a character in one of the fables you have just read. For example, think about how Lion might tell the fable of "The Lion and the Mouse." He might begin, "I was snoozing under a rock one day, when all of a sudden, something plopped on my nose." Retell the fable from the point of view of your chosen character. Remember to use pronouns such as *I, me, my,* and *mine.*

- *Write Fable Reviews*

  With other group members, look in the library for retellings of Aesop's fables. Take time to look closely at the books. Compare and contrast the pictures. Compare and contrast the retellings of the same fables. Which books would you recommend, and why? Write your opinions. (In your reviews, make sure to include the title and the names of the author and illustrator.)

- *Compare and Contrast*

  Find a fable that tells about opposites. "The City Mouse and the Country Mouse" is one example. "The Ant and the Grasshopper" is another. After you read the fable, use a Venn diagram to list similarities and differences.

# Making Predictions

## Learn About Making Predictions

*Thinking about the strategy*

When you are reading a story, help yourself stay involved with the story. One way to do that is by **making predictions** as you read. A prediction is a guess about what will happen next.

To make a reasonable prediction, think about what the author tells you about the story. Think about what you know from your own life.

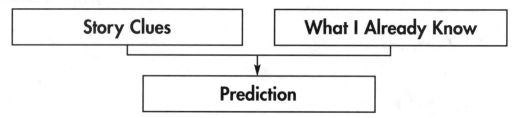

| Story Clues | What I Already Know |

**Prediction**

It doesn't matter if your prediction is wrong. As you get new information in the story, make new predictions. Then read on to check your predictions.

*Studying a model*

Read the beginning of the story and the notes beside it.

*Rosie's mother has allowed her to have lots of pets. I know that means her mother probably likes animals, too.*

*Rosie's mother thinks the kitten is cute. I know that her mother likes the kitten.*

"Rosie, are you hiding something under your jacket?" Rosie's mother asked sternly.

"I'm not really hiding it," Rosie replied. "I'm keeping it warm. It's one of Mr. Falco's kittens. He's giving them away."

"No, no! Not another animal!" said Rosie's mother. "You already have two parakeets, a gerbil, and a guinea pig. And Mittens might not want another cat in the house."

"But Mittens could use a playmate," said Rosie. "And just look at this lovable, fuzzy fellow." Rosie opened her jacket to show the kitten snuggling against her.

Rosie's mother sighed. "What a cute fluff ball he is!" she said, reaching out to stroke the kitten's head.

# Learn About a Graphic Organizer

*Understanding a prediction map*

A **prediction map** shows details that lead you to a prediction. Some details come from the story. Other details come from what you already know. A prediction map can help you make predictions as you read stories, fantasies, and other kinds of fiction.

Here is a prediction map for the story beginning on page 54.

*List facts and details from the story.*

*List what you know from your own experience.*

### In the Story

Rosie has parakeets, a gerbil, and a guinea pig.

Rosie says Mittens could use a playmate.

Words to describe a kitten: lovable, fuzzy, snuggling, cute fluff ball.

Rosie's mother sighs and reaches out to stroke the kitten.

### What I Already Know

People who have a lot of pets often want more pets.

Parents sometimes change their mind about not keeping a pet when they see how cute the pet is.

*Make a prediction based on story clues and what you know.*

### Prediction

Rosie's mother will let Rosie keep the kitten.

Filling out a prediction map can help you make reasonable guesses about what might happen next in a story.

*How can you find out if Rosie's mother will let Rosie keep the kitten?* You can read on to check your prediction and perhaps make a new one.

As you read, ask yourself

- What does the author tell me?
- What do I know about this kind of story or situation?
- What do I think will happen next?

# Learn About a Form of Writing

*Focusing on a play*

A **play** is a special kind of story. It is meant to be performed. Actors take the parts of the story characters. An audience follows the story by listening to what the actors say, noticing how they say it, and watching what they do.

A play has these features.

- It is written to tell the words the actors are to say.
- It often contains directions to the actors.
- It often describes the setting.

Read this part of a play. Notice the characters' names before the words they speak and the information in parentheses.

> WORKER: *(Brushing paint on park bench)* There! That's done. . . . Now, where did I put that Wet Paint sign? It must be in my truck. *(Exits)*
> BOY: *(Strolling with GIRL)* This bench is empty. Let's sit here.

*Organizing ideas in a prediction map*

You can use a prediction map to make predictions as you read a play. Here is a filled-in prediction map for the play above.

| In the Story | What I Already Know |
|---|---|
| Park bench is freshly painted. | Park bench is missing Wet Paint sign. |
| Worker leaves to find Wet Paint sign. | Boy and girl don't know the bench is freshly painted. |
| Boy suggests sitting on empty bench. | |

### Prediction

The boy and girl will sit on the bench and jump right up, with paint on their clothes.

# Prepare for the Reading Selection

*Gaining knowledge*

On the pages that follow, you will read an audio play. An audio play is intended to be read aloud, and possibly recorded. The audience is listening to the play, rather than watching it, so the actors must use their voices to tell the story. Sound effects also suggest action.

A silly or funny play is called a comedy. *I Scream for Ice Cream* is a comedy. The title is part of a chant that you may already know: "I scream, you scream, we all scream for ice cream." When you read the play, you may discover why ice cream might make someone scream.

As you read the play, make predictions. Then read on to check your predictions and make new ones.

## Learn Vocabulary

*Understanding vocabulary*

The boxed words below are **boldfaced** in the selection. Learn the meaning of each word. Then write the word or words that could replace the underlined word or words in the sentence.

| humorous |
| gift certificate |
| enthusiastically |
| generous |
| supreme |

1. Thank you for your <u>kind</u> gift. _____

2. The gold ribbon is the <u>top</u> award. _____

3. Everyone clapped <u>with great pleasure</u>. _____

4. The girl told the story in a <u>joking</u> way. _____

5. This <u>paper listing a dollar amount</u> works just like cash at the store.

_____

Read the first part of the play *I Scream for Ice Cream*.

## I Scream for Ice Cream

### An Audio Play

### Characters

JAN *(could be played by a boy or a girl)*
LEE *(Jan's friend; could be played by
a boy or a girl)*
MOM *(Jan's mother)*
DEENA *(owner of an ice cream shop)*

*MUSIC is played briefly where noted, to show that time is passing. The music can be live or recorded, but should be lighthearted and* **humorous***. Playful instruments, such as a kazoo, a xylophone, and a triangle, might work well.*

LEE: Happy birthday, Jan! Here's your present.

JAN: Thanks, Lee. I don't like to put things off, so I'll open it right now.
*(SOUND: RIPPING PAPER)* Let me see. This looks like a **gift certificate**. *(Reading)*
"This certificate entitles the bearer to delicious delights at Deena's Delicious
Ice Cream Shop. . . . Ten dollars." **(Enthusiastically)** Wow! That'll buy a ton
of ice cream.

LEE: So you like the present?

JAN: I *do* like it! I can never get enough ice cream. It's my favorite treat.
I could eat it for breakfast, lunch, dinner, and in between.

LEE: Especially on a hot day.

JAN: Like today.

LEE: *(Sighs)* You could fry an egg on the sidewalk today. It's got to be over
one hundred degrees.

JAN: In the shade.

LEE: I don't see any shade. By the way, why are we sitting out here
in the broiling sun?

JAN: It's even hotter inside.

LEE: What time is your party?

JAN: It's not really a party. Just a few kids coming over around three o'clock.
My mom will serve some snacks on a picnic table at the playground.

LEE: So we've got a little over an hour. What do you want to do?

JAN: It would be nice to go somewhere to cool off.

LEE: Somewhere air-conditioned.

JAN: Stores have air conditioning. *(With a sly voice)* Yesss . . . a store. I'm picturing one store in particular. A store that sells a favorite treat of mine. A favorite treat that I can now buy because I have enough money right here *(SOUND: TAPPING NOISES ON PAPER)*, thanks to my **generous** pal. . . . Can you guess what I'm thinking?

LEE: It's not too hard to do.

JAN: *(Calling)* Mom? Mom?

MOM: What is it?

JAN: Can I go over to First Avenue with Lee?

MOM: OK. Just be sure to be back by three.

JAN and LEE: *(Together)* We will. . . . *(Chanting)* I scream, you scream, we all scream for ice cream.

*(SOUNDS: FOOTSTEPS ON SIDEWALK START OUT LOUD AND THEN SLOWLY GROW SOFTER AS IF MORE DISTANT, AS DO CHANTING VOICES OF JAN AND LEE)*

JAN and LEE: *(Together, gradually becoming softer)* I scream, you scream, we all scream for ice cream! I scream, you scream, we all scream for ice cream! I scream, you scream, we all scream for . . .

*(MUSIC . . . FADES OUT)*

---

*Completing a prediction map*

Finish filling in the prediction map for the first part of the play. Then turn the page and read on to check your prediction.

| **In the Story** | **What I Already Know** |
|---|---|
| Jan has a ten-dollar gift certificate for Deena's Delicious Ice Cream Shop.<br><br>Ice cream is Jan's favorite treat. | Ice cream tastes good on a hot day. |

**Prediction**

LEE: Look at the list of flavors on that sign. Have you tried them all?

JAN: Yep. But I've always wanted to try the special banana boat **supreme**.

DEENA: *(Loudly)* Next! . . . What'll you have?

JAN: The special banana boat supreme, please.

DEENA: That comes with four flavors.

JAN: OK. I'll have the marshmallow caramel chip, the cherry pecan crunch, the strawberry coconut, and the peanut butter vanilla.

DEENA: Do you want whipped cream and strawberry sauce?

JAN: Yes, please.

DEENA: Three bananas or two?

JAN: Three, please.

LEE: *(Quietly, to JAN)* That costs five dollars, including tax.

JAN: I still have five dollars left. *(Calling to DEENA)* Better make two of them! *(Speaking again to LEE)* That way we can each have one.

DEENA: Here you are. I hope you two have a few friends waiting outside to share those.

JAN: Don't worry. We can handle these babies, no problem.

LEE: Well, here goes. MMMM. *(With full mouth)* Dee-lish!

JAN: MMMM. This tastes great. Let's dig in!

*(SOUNDS: LOUD EATING NOISES: SLURPS, GOBBLES, GRUNTS, SNORTS, GULPS, AND SO ON)*

*(MUSIC . . . FADES OUT)*

---

*Using a prediction map*

Think about what has happened since your last prediction. Fill in this prediction map, and make a new prediction.

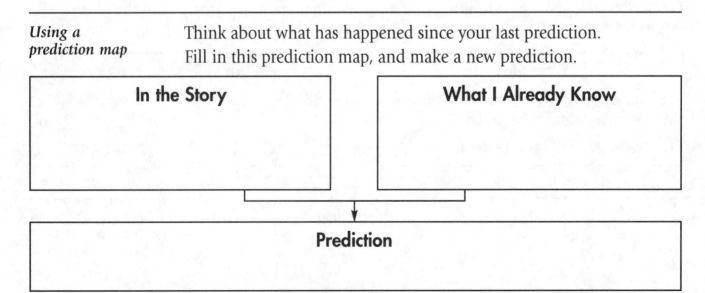

**In the Story**

**What I Already Know**

**Prediction**

## Reading Selection—Part Two

Read the second part of the play *I Scream for Ice Cream.*

LEE: *(Moaning)* I can't take another mouthful.

JAN: *(Moaning)* I can't believe I ate it all!

LEE: Ooh, my stomach hurts. My head hurts. My teeth hurt.

JAN: Ooh, mine too. I never want to see ice cream again.

LEE: I never want to hear the words *ice cream* again.

JAN: It's almost three. We'd better get back.

*(SOUNDS:SLOW FOOTSTEPS ON SIDEWALK; MOANING, GROANING)*

*(MUSIC . . . FADES OUT)*

MOM: Oh, here you two are. Happy birthday, honey! Look what I made for you and your friends.

JAN: Ooooh! Can it be what I think it is?

LEE: *(Groaning)* It is!

MOM: You've always said you wanted it. It's called a special banana boat supreme!

JAN and LEE: *(Together)* Aaaaaaargh!

*Using a prediction map*

Look back at the prediction you wrote on page 60. Did you predict what would happen? Now write what happened in the second part of the story.

_____

_____

_____

_____

_____

## Check Your Understanding

Think about what you've read. Then answer these questions.

1. As Jan and Lee start eating their ice cream, they make humorous sounds that are supposed to be
   - Ⓐ funny.
   - Ⓑ soft.
   - Ⓒ painful.
   - Ⓓ polite.

2. Why does Lee say, "You could fry an egg on the sidewalk today"?
   - Ⓐ Lee is always thinking of food.
   - Ⓑ Lee is describing the heat.
   - Ⓒ Lee is describing something seen earlier.
   - Ⓓ Lee wants to see whether an egg would fry.

3. Jan calls Lee a generous pal because Lee
   - Ⓐ gave her a gift worth ten dollars.
   - Ⓑ likes to eat ice cream.
   - Ⓒ is an old friend.
   - Ⓓ is the same age as Jan.

4. Which of these is not a story clue that you could have used to predict that Jan and Lee will go for ice cream?
   - Ⓐ Lee gives Jan a gift certificate.
   - Ⓑ Jan pictures a store that sells a favorite treat.
   - Ⓒ Jan and Lee say a chant that starts "I scream, you scream, we all scream, . . . "
   - Ⓓ Mom says to be back by three.

5. Jan orders four unusual ice-cream flavors, along with strawberry sauce and
   - Ⓐ chopped nuts and two bananas.
   - Ⓑ whipped cream and candy crunch.
   - Ⓒ whipped cream, pecan candy crunch, and a banana.
   - Ⓓ whipped cream and three bananas.

6. The name of the ice-cream dish is "special banana boat supreme." The word *supreme* suggests
   - Ⓐ its large size.
   - Ⓑ its sweetness.
   - Ⓒ the different flavors.
   - Ⓓ the price.

7. A second special banana boat supreme is ordered because
   - Ⓐ Jan wants Lee to have one, too.
   - Ⓑ Jan plans to eat both of them.
   - Ⓒ Jan has finished one and is ready to eat a second.
   - Ⓓ the first one is smaller than expected.

8. Deena says, "I hope you two have a few friends waiting outside to share those." That clue helps you figure out that
   - Ⓐ Deena sees their friends outside the store.
   - Ⓑ most people do not eat a special banana boat supreme all by themselves.
   - Ⓒ Deena knows that Jan is having a party.
   - Ⓓ Jan and Lee do not plan to share at all.

9. Which of these events happens last?
   - (A) Mom makes a banana boat supreme.
   - (B) Jan orders a banana boat supreme.
   - (C) Jan opens a gift from Lee.
   - (D) Jan and Lee chant as they walk to Fifth Avenue.

10. What might happen after the play ends?
    - (A) Jan will ask for more ice cream.
    - (B) Lee will go home angry.
    - (C) Jan and Lee will not be able to eat any more ice cream.
    - (D) Mom will serve dinner to Jan's friends.

11. What is the author's main reason for writing this play?
    - (A) to convince you that ice cream is bad for you
    - (B) to describe scenes clearly
    - (C) to make an audience laugh
    - (D) to give information and explain ideas

12. What is the main lesson this play teaches?
    - (A) Sweet things are bad for the teeth.
    - (B) Don't try to bite off more than you can chew.
    - (C) Good friends give good gifts.
    - (D) Too much of a good thing is not good.

## Extend Your Learning

- *Perform the Play*

  Perform the play *I Scream for Ice Cream*. First, decide who will read the parts of Jan, Lee, Mom, and Deena and who will make the sound effects and music. Practice by reading the play through several times. Then read aloud to an audience, or tape-record your performance.

- *Read Another Play*

  Ask a librarian for help in finding a collection of plays for young readers. Start by choosing one that seems interesting. As you read it, find good places to stop and make a prediction. (The end of a scene is usually a good stopping place.) Fill out a prediction map. Then write a few sentences to tell how well you predicted the ending of the play.

- *Write a Telephone Skit*

  Imagine a telephone conversation between two characters. What are they saying? Write the conversation as a very short, humorous play. Remember to include each character's name, any directions about the spoken words, and the exact words that each character says.

# Finding Word Meaning in Context

## Learn About Finding Word Meaning in Context

*Thinking about the strategy*

When you read, you may not understand the meaning of every word in a selection. To find the meaning of words you don't know, you can look for **context clues** in surrounding words and phrases. Often, you can find context clues in the same sentence as the word. Sometimes, you have to look at sentences that come before and after the word.

Here are some different kinds of context clues that you can use to figure out the meaning of a new or an unknown word.

| CONTEXT CLUES | EXAMPLES |
|---|---|
| Synonym (a word that means the same) | He calls himself a **spy**, but some call him a **snoop**. |
| Antonym (a word that means the opposite) | That plant is **artificial** although it looks **real**. |
| Definition | A **consumer** is *a person who buys things*. |
| Examples | She has worked for many **politicians**, including the **mayor**, the **governor**, and two **senators**. |

You can also get clues to a word's meaning by thinking about the way the word is used in the sentence and what all the other words are about. To be sure of a word's meaning, you can look in a dictionary.

*Studying a model*

Read the paragraph and the notes beside it.

Bright *and* cheerful *are context clues to the meaning of* dreary.

Change *is a context clue to the meaning of* transform.

When we moved into the old house, the living room was dark and dreary. Mom said we could change that easily. "A fresh coat of paint will transform this into a bright, cheerful space," she said. "To add warmth and light up the room, we'll use candles and small lamps."

# Learn About a Graphic Organizer

*Understanding a words-and-meaning chart*

A **words-and-meaning chart** will help you keep track of new words and context clues so that you can figure out the meaning of the new words. You can use a words-and-meaning chart every time you read. Sometimes, you may just write the word in the chart and come back later to figure out its meaning. Other times, you may want to figure out the meaning of the word before you continue reading.

Here is a words-and-meaning chart for the paragraph on page 64. It shows context clues and what the reader thinks the word means based on those context clues.

*List new or unknown words here.* ▼

*Find clues to a word's meaning in surrounding words and phrases. List them here.* ▼

*Think about the context clues. Then write what you think the word means.* ▼

| Word | Context Clues | What I Think Word Means |
|------|---------------|-------------------------|
| dreary | dark; bright, cheerful | gloomy; not cheery |
| transform | change; fresh paint | to change or make different |

When you complete a words-and-meaning chart, you use context clues to find the meaning of a word. You better understand what the sentence, paragraph, or whole selection is about.

*Why isn't Mom upset about the dark living room?*
Mom has a plan for making the room bright and cheerful.

As you read, ask yourself

- How is the new word used in the sentence?
- What words around the new word give clues to its meaning?
- How can I be sure of a word's meaning?

# Learn About a Form of Writing

*Focusing on an informational article*

An **informational article** explains a topic using facts, details, and examples. An informational article may be on any topic. For example, an author might write about a person or an event in history. Many informational articles, however, are about science or nature.

An informational article often has these features.

- It uses facts, details, and examples to help explain a topic.

- It may contain photographs or other visuals to help explain ideas.

- Its main purpose is to give information about the topic.

Here is the opening paragraph of an informational article about an unusual ape.

> At first glance, a bonobo looks like a chimpanzee. Look again. The bonobo is much smaller than a chimp. For this reason, bonobos are sometimes called pygmy chimpanzees. Bonobos are different from chimps in other ways, too. For example, a bonobo's skin has a darker hue, or color, than a chimp's skin. Also, a chimp's nose and mouth stick out while a bonobo's face does not protrude as much.

*Organizing ideas in a words-and-meaning chart*

You can use a words-and-meaning chart to find the meaning of new words in an informational article. Understanding the meaning of these words will give you a better understanding of the topic and will make the article more interesting. Here is a filled-in words-and-meaning chart for the paragraph above.

| Word | Context Clues | What I Think Word Means |
|------|---------------|-------------------------|
| pygmy | much smaller | something smaller than usual |
| hue | color; darker | color or shade |
| protrude | nose and mouth stick out | stick out; push out |

# Prepare for the Reading Selection

*Gaining knowledge*

Some animals find ways to keep warm by using the world around them. Chimpanzees and orangutans often make sleeping nests in trees. On cool nights, they make blankets of leaves or grass to wrap around themselves. Macaques, monkeys that are found high in the mountains of northern Japan, have thick fur coats that keep them warm. Sometimes, though, it is so cold that even their fur isn't enough to keep them warm. Instead, they bathe in nearby hot volcanic springs. In the article you will read on the pages that follow, you will learn of the different and interesting ways that other animals cool off and stay warm.

# Learn Vocabulary

*Understanding vocabulary*

The boxed words below are **boldfaced** in the selection. Learn the meaning of each word. Then write the word that matches the clue.

| |
|---|
| extreme |
| rely |
| provides |
| exposed |
| insulation |
| related |

1. What word means "put out in the open air?"

   _____

2. What word means the same as *depend*?

   _____

3. What stops cold air from getting into your home?

   _____

4. What word describes two people who are cousins?

   _____

5. How might you describe very hot or very cold weather?

   _____

6. What word belongs with *supplies, gives,* and *offers*?

   _____

Read the first part of the informational article "Animals: Hot and Cold"

## Animals: Hot and Cold

Animals inhabit all parts of the world. They live in dry, hot deserts and steamy rainforests. They live in the freezing tundra of the North and South Poles. They live at cold, windy mountaintops and at the chilled depths of the oceans.

Humans are animals, too, and they live in many of these **extreme** environments. Humans, however, have the use of air conditioners, electric fans, heaters, fireplaces, hats, and gloves. Other animals can't use such items to cool or warm themselves. Instead, they must **rely** on natural methods to cope with the extreme temperatures throughout the world.

Animals have many ways to keep cool. Some use special body parts. African elephants have mammoth ears that are each about 6 feet across, or about the size of a bed sheet. To cool themselves in the heat, they flap their giant ears to create a cooling breeze.

Other animals also use their ears to cool themselves. The jackrabbit, kit fox, and fennec fox have long ears. When breezes blow across their ears, the blood in their ears is cooled. This helps to cool their whole bodies.

Desert birds have long legs that work like the ears of the jackrabbit, kit fox, and fennec fox. When cool air passes over their long, featherless legs, their blood cools.

Some animals use their tails to stay cool. The ground squirrel, which lives in the Kalahari Desert in Africa, holds its tail above its head like an umbrella. This **provides** the squirrel with shade from the hot desert sun.

Sweating also cools most animals' bodies. When sweat evaporates, or escapes into the air, it cools the skin. Kangaroos in Australia use evaporation another way. They spread their saliva over their bodies with their tongues. They lick their paws and rub the saliva over their faces. When the saliva evaporates, their skin is cooled.

The land itself helps animals stay cool in hot climates. Gerbils that live in the Kara-Kum Desert in Asia dig tunnels. They burrow down only 4 inches to find temperatures more than 60°F cooler than above the ground. Some desert birds also cool off in underground burrows. Others sit in the cool shade of rocks.

*Completing a words-and-meaning chart*

Some of the words-and-meaning chart for the first part of the informational article has been filled in. Complete the chart with more words that are new or unknown to you.

| Word | Context Clues | What I Think Word Means |
|---|---|---|
| inhabit | parts of the world; live | live in a certain place |
| tundra | freezing; North and South poles | land that is frozen and covered with ice |
| depths | mountaintops; oceans | the deep part of the ocean |
|  |  |  |
|  |  |  |
|  |  |  |
|  |  |  |
|  |  |  |
|  |  |  |

Read the second part of the informational article "Animals: Hot and Cold."

Animals have several ways to keep their bodies warm in cold weather. Mostly, they use fur, feathers, and body fat. The musk ox, found in Greenland, has very long fur. Its hair can grow up to 35 inches long. This thick, warm coat helps the musk ox survive temperatures as cold as −60°F. The wild yak of Tibet and China can live as high as 20,000 feet in the mountains. A long, thick coat keeps the wild yak warm.

Certain squirrels use their long, bushy tails to stay warm in winter. They wrap their tails around themselves like cozy fur coats. Snowshoe rabbits have very long hairs on their feet. The hairs grow over their feet and in between their toes. This keeps their feet warm in the snow.

Some animals have more than one way to stay warm. The arctic fox has a thick coat of fur, hair on its feet, and furry ears. It also has a short nose. This small muzzle helps stop heat loss because only a small area of the fox's face is **exposed** to cold winds.

Animals can also use feathers to keep warm. The emperor penguin spends a lot of time in the frigid water of Antarctica. It often stays underwater for 10 to 20 minutes at a time. In between its deep dives, the emperor penguin combs its feathers. This traps air in the feathers. The trapped air provides a layer of **insulation** that keeps the penguin warm.

Marine mammals have a special layer of fat beneath their skin, called blubber. This blubber keeps them warm when they are in cold water. Weddell seals live farther south than any other mammal on earth. They spend large amounts of time diving beneath the polar ice. Some Weddell seals stay under the ice for over an hour at a time. Their blubber helps them to survive the freezing Antarctic water.

Some animals warm themselves too well. The vicuña, which is **related** to the camel, lives in the Andes Mountains in South America. This animal has a very warm coat of fur. It also has hairless areas on its legs. When the vicuña gets too warm in its fur, it stands in the wind and lets the air cool the blood in its legs.

*Using a words-and-meaning chart*

Fill in the words-and-meaning chart to find the meaning of new or unknown words from the second part of the informational article.

| Word | Context Clues | What I Think Word Means |
| --- | --- | --- |
|  |  |  |
|  |  |  |
|  |  |  |
|  |  |  |
|  |  |  |

## Check Your Understanding

Think about what you've read. Then answer these questions.

1. What is Part One of the article mostly about?
   - (A) how humans stay warm
   - (B) how humans keep cool
   - (C) how animals stay warm
   - (D) how animals keep cool

2. Which of these might be called extreme?
   - (A) a soft breeze
   - (B) a warm afternoon
   - (C) a freezing cold day
   - (D) a light rain

3. Which word in Part One gives a clue to the meaning of *mammoth*?
   - (A) giant
   - (C) body
   - (B) flap
   - (D) cooling

4. According to the author, how are some desert birds and gerbils alike?
   - (A) They both use their tails to stay cool.
   - (B) They both cool off underground.
   - (C) They both depend on their long legs to stay cool.
   - (D) They both use their saliva to stay cool.

5. From the article, you can figure out that
   - (A) it's very cold at 20,000 feet in the mountains.
   - (B) the temperature never goes above –60°F in Greenland.
   - (C) wild yaks cannot live in warm climates.
   - (D) there are only a few musk ox in Greenland.

6. Which of these animals does not use its ears to cool itself?
   - (A) African elephant
   - (B) kit fox
   - (C) ground squirrel
   - (D) jackrabbit

7. In Part Two, you can tell that the word *survive* means
   - (A) "to grow hair."
   - (B) "to stay warm."
   - (C) "to keep away from."
   - (D) "to live through."

8. Why do snowshoe rabbits have warm feet even in the snow?
   - (A) They wear snowshoes.
   - (B) Their tails wrap around their feet.
   - (C) Long hairs grow over their feet and between their toes.
   - (D) They lick their paws.

9. Something that acts like insulation helps
   - (A) sea animals to dive deeper.
   - (B) trap warm air close to an animal's body.
   - (C) hair grow faster on some animals.
   - (D) outside temperatures go up and down.

10. The vicuña and the camel are related, which means that they
    - (A) are in the same animal family.
    - (B) are the same exact animal.
    - (C) are both tall and hairless.
    - (D) have been around for thousands of years.

72

**11.** Which of these statements is an opinion?

Ⓐ The hair of the musk ox can grow up to 35 inches long.

Ⓑ The vicuña lives in the Andes Mountains in South America.

Ⓒ An emperor penguin can stay under water for 10 minutes.

Ⓓ Some animals warm themselves too well.

**12.** The author wrote this article mainly

Ⓐ to describe animals with unusual features.

Ⓑ to explain how some animals cool and warm themselves.

Ⓒ to entertain readers with an interesting story about animals and weather.

Ⓓ to persuade readers to dress warmly in cold weather.

## Extend Your Learning

- *Read About Animals*

  Work with a partner to list all the animals mentioned in "Animals: Hot and Cold." Then choose two or three of the animals to learn more about. Look in science books, a nature encyclopedia, or on the Internet for information. As you read, jot down any new or unknown words in a words-and-meaning chart. Then use context clues to figure out the meaning of the words.

- *Write an Informational Article*

  Write an informational article. The article might explain an unusual animal, like the bonobo ape described on page 66, or it might explain the unusual ways some animals do things. For example, you might tell how some animals prepare homes for their young. You might tell how some egg-laying animals take care of their eggs. In a group, brainstorm a list of ideas. Then choose your favorite idea to research and write about.

- *Paint a Mural*

  With your class, paint a mural that shows how some animals stay cool or keep warm. You can look over the informational article "Animals: Hot and Cold" for the kinds of animals to include in your mural.

# LESSON 8 Drawing Conclusions and Making Inferences

## Learn About Drawing Conclusions and Making Inferences

*Thinking about the strategy*

Authors do not always tell you every detail that you want to know about the characters, setting (where and when the story takes place), and events in a story. Sometimes, you have to **draw conclusions** or **make inferences** about the details that the author has left out.

To draw conclusions or make inferences

- **Identify** the details that the author has given about characters, setting, and events.
- **Think about** what you already know from your own life.
- **Put together** story clues and what you know to figure out details the author has not told you.

Do not confuse a conclusion with a prediction. A conclusion is something that you can be almost certain is true if you use the correct information. A prediction is what you think will happen sometime in the future. A prediction may or may not happen.

*Studying a model*

Read the story and the notes beside it.

*The author gives these clues: backpacks, snack, homework.*

*You know that children often carry backpacks to and from school. You know that children often eat snacks and do homework after school.*

*One conclusion you can draw is that Sid and Ben have just come from school.*

Sid and Ben dropped their backpacks on the hall bench. "I'm starved," Sid said. "Let's get a snack before we start our homework."

A few minutes later, Sid and Ben were at the kitchen table. Ben was about to bite into his apple when Sid's dog Puff dashed over to the pantry door and began to bark.

"What's wrong with Puff?" Ben asked.

"Nothing," Sid said. "He just wants a snack, too."

Sid got up and opened the pantry door.

# Learn About a Graphic Organizer

*Understanding a conclusions/ inferences diagram*

A **conclusions/inferences diagram** can help you figure out details that an author has not told you. You can use a conclusions/ inferences diagram to draw conclusions or make inferences when reading stories, fables, narratives, articles, and biographies.

Here is a conclusions/inferences diagram for the story on page 74.

*List details the author gives about story characters, setting, and events.*

| **Story Clues** | **What I Know** |
|---|---|
| Sid and Ben have backpacks. They have a snack before doing homework. Puff barks at the pantry door. Sid says Puff wants a snack. | Children carry backpacks to and from school. Children often eat snacks and do homework after school. Some people keep dog treats in a food pantry. |

*Write what you know from your own life.*

*Think about people, places, and events that you know.*

*Put together story clues and what you know to draw conclusions.*

| **What I Can Figure Out** |
|---|
| Sid and Ben have just come from school. Puff's dog treats are in the pantry. |

When you fill in a conclusions/inferences diagram, you figure out details that the author does not give or completely explain in a story.

*Why does Puff bark at the pantry door?*
Puff has probably been given treats many times. Puff knows that the treats are in the pantry. He barks to let Sid know he wants a treat.

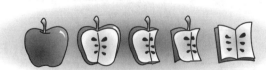

**As you read, ask yourself**

- What story clues does the author give?
- What do I know from my own life?
- What can I figure out from story clues and what I know?

# Learn About a Form of Writing

A **personal narrative** is a story an author tells about his or her own life. The story is usually about something important to the author.

A personal narrative often has these features.

- It uses the first-person personal pronouns *I*, *me*, and *we*.

- Like other stories, it has a beginning, a middle, and an end.

- Its main purpose is usually to entertain.

Read this paragraph from a personal narrative by Elijah Moore.

> I never liked moving, but my father's job was to set up new businesses. When the business was running smoothly, his work was done. Then he had to start over with a new business. Sometimes, the company was nearby. Most of the time, it was in another state. One day, my father announced he had changed jobs, and we were moving for the last time.

*Organizing ideas in a conclusions/inferences diagram*
You can use a conclusions/inferences diagram to figure out details that the author does not tell you in a personal narrative. Here is a filled-in conclusions/inferences diagram for the paragraph above.

| Story Clues | What I Know |
|---|---|
| I never liked moving.<br>Father set up businesses in different states.<br>Father announced he had changed jobs, and we were moving for the last time. | Usually, when a parent's job takes him or her to a new place, the family moves.<br>Children are usually glad to live in the same place for a long time. |

**What I Can Figure Out**

The speaker and his family probably moved many times to different states.
The speaker was probably glad when his father said they were moving for the last time.

# Prepare for the Reading Selection

*Gaining knowledge*

In the 1770s, a group of American colonists formed a volunteer military company. These men claimed to be ready to go into battle at a minute's notice. As a result, they were called minutemen.

At dawn, on April 19, 1775, minutemen gathered from several towns in Massachusetts. Together they marched to the towns of Concord and Lexington. There they faced British troops in the first battles of the Revolutionary War. The Revolutionary War lasted almost eight years. It ended in 1783, when the United States and Great Britain signed a peace treaty. The story you will read on the following pages recalls the minutemen and the Revolution.

## Learn Vocabulary

*Understanding vocabulary*

The boxed words below are **boldfaced** in the selection. Learn the meaning of each word. Then write the word beside its definition.

| |
|---|
| rural |
| descendants |
| display |
| gigantic |
| memorize |
| quiz |

1. to learn by heart _____

2. family members _____

3. huge _____

4. to ask questions _____

5. having to do with the country _____

6. to show _____

Read the first part of the personal narrative "The Flag."

## The Flag

The summer before I was in third grade, we moved to a small **rural** New England town. I had never seen my mother so excited. "Can you believe it?" she said. "On April 19, 1775, at the top of this very street, our street, the minutemen mustered." I pictured grown men, covering themselves with mustard. Mom's face glowed as she continued. "From there, of course, they marched to the Concord Bridge to face the British army."

I learned later that *mustered* means "to gather together." I also learned that some of the people who live in our town are **descendants** of the original minutemen. The town is very proud of the role its early citizens played in the Revolutionary War. Each spring, it holds a fair to honor those soldiers.

The Minuteman Day Fair starts with a parade that goes from Town Hall to the fairgrounds. Men and boys dressed as minutemen, the fire and police departments, town officials, and the school band take part. At the end of the parade, groups of children ride decorated bicycles.

At the fairgrounds, children take part in ball games, pie-eating contests, and relay races. Local artists and crafts persons **display** their works. The town's firefighters cook and sell hamburgers, hotdogs, and corn on the cob.

Later in the day, town leaders give out two important awards. First, the Golden Patriot Award is given to a person who has worked hard for the town. Then a **gigantic** American flag is presented to the winner of the third-grade flag contest.

My third-grade teacher was Mr. Samuels. In early spring, he explained the contest to us. Then he showed us the flag that would go to the winner. The moment I saw that flag, I made up my mind to win it. All I had to do was get the highest score on the flag test.

"How much could there be to learn about the flag?" I thought. I soon found out.

Every day, for the next few weeks, I came home from school with facts and details about the American flag. I had worksheets about the different designs of the flag through the years. I had notes about rules for hanging flags. I had facts about flagmakers. Soon, I had enough flag information to fill a book!

*Completing a conclusions/ inferences diagram*

Some of the conclusions/inferences diagram has been filled in. Add more details from the first part of the personal narrative and what you know from your own life to draw conclusions or make inferences about the characters, setting, and events.

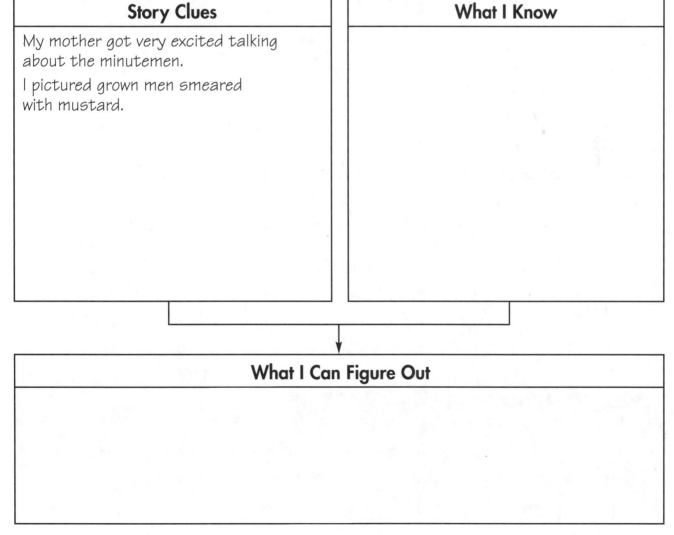

### Story Clues

My mother got very excited talking about the minutemen.

I pictured grown men smeared with mustard.

### What I Know

### What I Can Figure Out

Read the second part of the personal narrative "The Flag."

Each night, Mom helped me study and **memorize** all of that information. One night, she picked up a worksheet. It listed the dates that each flag design was in use. She began to **quiz** me on the dates.

"Mom, I don't have to know that," I said. "Those dates won't be on the test! Besides, I can't fit one more fact about flags into my brain."

"Danielle," she replied calmly, "you should learn these dates."

"But, Mom! I don't have to learn them," I cried.

"Danielle," she said, "if you are going to learn about something, don't you think you should learn as much as you can?"

So, mostly to please my mom, I learned all those dates.

On the day of the test, I gripped my pencil so tightly my hand began to hurt. I loosened my grip, took three deep breaths, and began the test. Finally, I turned to the last page of the test. At the top I saw *Extra Credit* and four questions. Each had to do with the dates of the different flag designs!

A week later, students from both third grades gathered in our classroom to find out who won the flag contest. Mr. Samuels announced the second-place and third-place winners first. Bonnie Chung came in third. She had a total score of 98 points. Adam Taylor came in second. He had a total score of 100 points.

Then Mr. Samuels cleared his throat. "The first-place winner," he said, "with a score of 103 points, is Danielle Stevens!"

I couldn't believe it. I was ready to burst!

After school, I jumped off the bus and ran all the way down our street. I couldn't wait to tell my mother the news. Mom gave me a big hug. "I knew you could do it!" she said.

Later, I looked carefully at my test, which Mr. Samuels had marked. I added up the points. I'd gotten one question wrong. However, I'd answered all four extra-credit questions correctly. I realized that without the extra-credit, I would have had only ninety-nine points. I would have come in second instead of first.

The following Saturday was the Minuteman Day Fair. I stood proudly in front of neighbors, classmates, teachers, friends, and family. Mr. Robinson, the police chief, gave me my flag. "Thank you, Chief Robinson," I said politely. Then I turned and smiled at my mother. "Most of all, thank you, Mom."

---

*Using a conclusions/ inferences diagram*

Use information from the second part of the narrative to fill in the conclusions/inferences diagram.

| Story Clues | What I Know |
|---|---|
|  |  |

**What I Can Figure Out**

## Check Your Understanding

Think about what you've read. Then answer these questions.

1. Because Danielle lives in a rural town, she probably sees a lot of
   - Ⓐ tall buildings.
   - Ⓒ heavy traffic.
   - Ⓑ trees and grass.
   - Ⓓ ships.

2. In the personal narrative, the best meaning of the word *mustered* is
   - Ⓐ "to cover oneself with mustard."
   - Ⓑ "to be brave."
   - Ⓒ "to gather for battle."
   - Ⓓ "to grow up."

3. Which of these statements is an opinion?
   - Ⓐ On April 19, 1775, the minutemen mustered.
   - Ⓑ The minutemen marched to the Concord Bridge.
   - Ⓒ Each spring, the town holds a fair to honor the minutemen.
   - Ⓓ The town is very proud of its early citizens.

4. Which of these does not happen on the day of the Minuteman Day Fair?
   - Ⓐ People march in a parade.
   - Ⓑ Children take part in relay races.
   - Ⓒ The third graders take a flag test.
   - Ⓓ Town leaders give awards.

5. From the personal narrative, you can tell that Danielle
   - Ⓐ thought it would be easy to learn about the flag.
   - Ⓑ cannot remember details.
   - Ⓒ did not enjoy history.
   - Ⓓ hoped to win the Golden Patriot Award some day.

6. A gigantic flag is very
   - Ⓐ colorful.
   - Ⓑ large.
   - Ⓒ old.
   - Ⓓ dirty.

7. Danielle had to memorize facts about the flag. She had to
   - Ⓐ learn and remember facts.
   - Ⓑ write a list of facts.
   - Ⓒ find facts.
   - Ⓓ prove the facts were true.

8. From the personal narrative, you can tell that on the day of the test, Danielle is
   - Ⓐ sad.
   - Ⓑ angry.
   - Ⓒ tired.
   - Ⓓ nervous.

9. In the personal narrative, the words *I was ready to burst* mean that Danielle
   - Ⓐ "swelled up like a balloon."
   - Ⓑ "spoke too loudly."
   - Ⓒ "was filled with joy."
   - Ⓓ "wanted to go home."

10. What happened because Danielle learned the flag design dates?
    - Ⓐ She carried the flag in the parade.
    - Ⓑ She won the flag.
    - Ⓒ She fell asleep during the flag test.
    - Ⓓ She got the Golden Patriot Award.

**11.** Which of these events happened last?

   Ⓐ  Danielle took the flag test.

   Ⓑ  Minutemen faced the British army.

   Ⓒ  Mr. Samuels showed students the flag prize.

   Ⓓ  Students from both third grades gathered in Danielle's classroom.

**12.** The author wrote this personal narrative mainly to

   Ⓐ  entertain readers with a story about a special event in her life.

   Ⓑ  persuade readers to learn more about the flag.

   Ⓒ  explain how the Revolutionary War started.

   Ⓓ  describe the flag.

## Extend Your Learning

- *Read a Story*

    Fill in a conclusions/inferences diagram for a story your class has read. As you read, jot down story clues and what you know from your own life. Then use these notes to draw conclusions or make inferences about the setting, characters, and events in the story. In a small group, compare your conclusions and inferences with classmates.

- *Write a Personal Narrative*

    Write a personal narrative about a special event in your life. Before you write, try to answer these questions: *Who else was part of this event? Where did this event take place? Why is this event important to me? What difference has this event made in my life?* You may wish to take notes in a chart or a web. Then use your notes to write a lively story with interesting and colorful details. Remember that a personal narrative tells a story, using the personal pronoun *I*.

- *Research Flag Facts*

    With a partner, do research to learn more about the American flag. Look in encyclopedias and on the Internet. Try to find at least five facts each. Then use these facts to make up a flag quiz. Challenge other students in the class to take your quiz.

# Distinguishing Between Fact and Opinion

## Learn About Distinguishing Between Fact and Opinion

*Thinking about the strategy*

When you read, you may come across statements that are facts and statements that are opinions. A **fact** is a statement that can be proved. You might prove a fact by looking in an encyclopedia. You might ask an expert. You might use your own eyes or ears.

An **opinion** is a statement that cannot be proved. Opinions tell what a person believes, thinks, or feels. Authors often use clue words such as *I think* and *I believe* to let the reader know that a statement is an opinion. Clue words such as *always* and *never* also signal opinions.

To distinguish between fact and opinion

- Look to see if the details in the statement can be proved or checked. Then it is a fact.

- Look to see if the statement tells what someone believes, thinks, or feels. Then it is an opinion.

- Look for clue words that signal opinions:

  | | | |
  |---|---|---|
  | *I think* | *always* | *all* |
  | *I believe* | *never* | *worst* |
  | *seems* | *best* | *greatest* |

---

*Studying a model*

Read the paragraph and the notes beside it.

*The statement about the list in the newspaper can be checked. This is a fact.*

*The words* favorite, I think, *and* I believe *signal statements of opinion.*

    Last week, *The Daily Sun* printed a list of polluted lakes, rivers, and streams in our region. Laurel River was at the top of the list. Laurel River was once a favorite place for families in our town to swim and fish. I think that we should all work together to make Laurel River safe and clean again. I also believe that people who pollute rivers, lakes, and streams should be punished.

# Learn About a Graphic Organizer

*Understanding a fact-and-opinion chart*

A **fact-and-opinion chart** will help you keep track of facts and opinions when you read. You can use a fact-and-opinion chart to distinguish between facts and opinions in fiction stories and nonfiction articles.

Here is a fact-and-opinion chart for the paragraph on page 84. It shows statements of fact and statements of opinion found in the paragraph.

*In this column, list statements that can be proved or checked.*

| FACT<br>*Can it be proved or checked?* | OPINION<br>*Is it what someone believes, thinks, or feels?* |
|---|---|
| Last week, The Daily Sun printed a list of polluted lakes, rivers, and streams.<br><br>Laurel River was at the top of the list. | Laurel River was once a favorite place to swim and fish.<br><br>I think that we should all work together.<br><br>I believe that people who pollute should be punished. |

*In this column, list statements that tell what the author believes, thinks, or feels.*

When you complete a fact-and-opinion chart, you distinguish between facts and opinions. This can help you recognize what the author wants you to understand.

*What does the author want you to understand about Laurel River?* Laurel River is polluted now, but people can work together to help make the river safe for swimming and fishing again. People who pollute should be punished.

**As you read, ask yourself**

- Can this statement be proved or checked?
- Does this statement tell what someone believes, thinks, or feels?
- Are there clue words that signal opinions?

# Learn About a Form of Writing

*Focusing on a feature story*

A **feature story** is a news article about a special person, place, event, or thing. The topic of a feature story is usually something that most newspaper or magazine readers will find interesting.

A feature story often has these elements.

- It is about a special person, place, event, or thing.
- It is often divided into parts. Each part may have a different focus.
- It usually has a headline that catches the reader's attention.
- It often presents facts along with the author's opinions.

Here is the opening paragraph of a feature story.

### Underwater Treasure Hunt

Deep-sea divers recently made an amazing discovery! They found the wreck of a Spanish ship that sank in 1724. The ship was half buried in mud. Divers spent weeks clearing away the mud and sand. How excited they became when they found diamonds, gold, silver, and other valuable items on board. It was one of the greatest treasures ever found!

*Organizing ideas in a fact-and-opinion chart*

You can use a fact-and-opinion chart when reading a feature story. Here is a filled-in fact-and-opinion chart for the paragraph above.

| FACT <br> *Can it be proved or checked?* | OPINION <br> *Is it what someone believes, thinks, or feels?* |
| --- | --- |
| Divers found the wreck of a Spanish ship that sank in 1724. | Deep-sea divers recently made an amazing discovery! |
| The ship was half buried in mud. | How excited they became. |
| Divers spent weeks clearing away the mud and sand. | It was one of the greatest treasures ever found! |

# Prepare for the Reading Selections

*Gaining knowledge*

In the feature stories you will read on the following pages, you will learn about a special underwater environment called a coral reef. Coral reefs exist in the warm, shallow waters of the Indian and Pacific oceans. Coral reefs are also found in the Caribbean Sea and in the Florida Keys in the Atlantic Ocean. As you will discover, coral are animals that need space and sunlight to grow. The shape and size of coral depend on the area where they grow. Some coral are thin and fragile. Some are thick and sturdy. Some are soft and lacy. Some are hard and pointy. Some coral grow fast while other coral grow more slowly. Coral come in a rich variety of colors, such as green, orange, and purple. The vivid colors seem to make the coral glow.

# Learn Vocabulary

*Understanding vocabulary*

The boxed words below are **boldfaced** in the selections. Learn the meaning of each word. Then write the word that matches the clue.

| structures |
| texture |
| attitude |
| diverse |
| complex |
| abounds |
| attract |

1. This is how something feels to touch. _____

2. Magnets do this. _____

3. This means "different." _____

4. This describes something that is not simple and has many parts. _____

5. These can be buildings or bridges. _____

6. This describes the way that people feel about something. _____

7. This can mean "overflows" or "is filled with." _____

Read the feature story "The Coral Reef Crisis" by Rita Upadhyay. This story first appeared in *Time for Kids*, November 10, 2000.

## The Coral Reef Crisis

Under the clear blue sea, busy communities of ocean creatures live together in brightly colored **structures** called coral reefs. These beautiful underwater cities have been around for millions of years.

But danger looms. In October 2000, scientists issued a strong warning. More than a quarter of the world's reefs have been destroyed by pollution and careless human behavior. If things don't improve quickly, all the reefs may die in the next 20 years. That would put thousands of sea creatures at risk of extinction.

### Precious Underwater Habitats

Coral seems like rock because of its stony **texture**, but it is actually made up of tiny clear animals called coral polyps. Millions of them stick together in colonies and form a hard shell. As colonies grow together, they make big reefs. The bright color of coral comes from tiny sea plants called algae. Coral and algae depend on each other to live. This is called symbiosis.

Coral may feel tough, but it's very sensitive. Pollution has hurt many reefs. Bad fishing methods, including the use of dynamite, have also caused terrible harm.

But the biggest threat is that oceans are getting warmer. Warm water causes coral to lose the algae that supply its food and color. This deadly process is called coral bleaching.

Scientists believe the reefs can still be saved if governments outlaw bad practices and control pollution. "The world's **attitude** must change," says scientist Clive Wilkinson.

*The Great Barrier Reef runs along the east coast of Australia. Scientists come from all over the world to study its exotic plant and animal life.*

**Word Watch**

*Algae*   Sea plants that give food and color to coral.

*Coral bleaching*   A harmful process caused by warm water. It destroys reefs by making them lose their color and food supply.

*Coral polyps*   Animals the size of a pinhead that join together to form coral reefs.

*Symbiosis*   When two plants and/or animals live together and depend on each other for survival.

---

*Completing a fact-and-opinion chart*

Some of the fact-and-opinion chart has been filled in. Add some more facts and opinions from the feature story.

| **FACT**<br>*Can it be proved or checked?* | **OPINION**<br>*Is it what someone believes, thinks, or feels?* |
| --- | --- |
| Communities of ocean creatures live together in coral reefs.<br><br>In October 2000, scientists issued a warning. | If things don't improve quickly, all the reefs may die in the next 20 years.<br><br>Coral seems like rock. |

Read the feature story "Life Abounds on Coral Reefs."

## Life Abounds on Coral Reefs

Coral reefs are often called "the rainforests of the ocean." That's because only in a rainforest is life as **diverse** as it is on a coral reef. Thousands of species, or kinds, of fish, plants, and other animals live on coral reefs. In fact, research suggests that 25% of all underwater sea life exists on the world's coral reefs. Yet, coral reefs cover less than 0.2% of the ocean floor!

Coral reefs, like rainforests, are **complex** ecosystems. In an ecosystem, plants, animals, and the environment work together to support life. And a close look shows that life **abounds** on a coral reef.

### Coral Reef Creatures

As many as 4,000 species of fish live on coral reefs. Among these are some of the most colorful fish in the world, such as angelfish, butterflyfish, clown fish, and parrotfish. The parrotfish got its name because its front teeth look like the beak of a parrot. Parrotfish use their strong teeth to bite and chew on hard coral. The algae in the coral helps feed the parrotfish.

Coral reefs also **attract** a variety of sharks that include nurse sharks, zebra sharks, and lemon sharks. Some sharks live on the coral reef. Some live near the coral reefs. For these sharks, the coral reef is like a fine restaurant. They swim in to dine from a menu of clams, shrimps, and other small sea creatures.

Another fish that lives on the coral reef is the eel. Eels are long and thin. This makes it easy for them to hide in the cracks of the reef. When crabs, octopuses, and other prey swim by, eels capture them in their powerful jaws.

*Colorful fish, sharks, starfish, sea horses, snails, urchins, and several kinds of sponges live on coral reefs. Sea cucumbers, snails, worms, and some sea turtles live there, too.*

One of the most helpful fish on coral reefs are wrasses. Bright and colorful and shaped like cigars, wrasses are sometimes called "cleaner fish." Wrasses place themselves along the reef. Large fish swim near the wrasses who peck at the bodies of the larger fish. As they peck, wrasses eat parasites, or germs, from the bodies of the larger fish. One wrasse can eat 1,200 parasites a day!

Plants, called sea grasses, also grow in and around coral reefs. These plants offer shelter and food to the thousands of creatures that call the coral reef home.

---

*Using a*
*fact-and-opinion chart*     Fill in the fact-and-opinion chart with facts and opinions from the feature story.

| **FACT** *Can it be proved or checked?* | **OPINION** *Is it what someone believes, thinks, or feels?* |
|---|---|
| | |

## Check Your Understanding

Think about what you've read. Then answer these questions.

1. "The Coral Reef Crisis" is mainly about
   Ⓐ beautiful underwater cities.
   Ⓑ sea plants called algae.
   Ⓒ dangers to coral reefs.
   Ⓓ extinct animals.

2. The texture of coral is stony, which means that coral
   Ⓐ is as hard as stone.
   Ⓑ has the feeling of stone.
   Ⓒ is as heavy as stone.
   Ⓓ contains stone.

3. Coral polyps are
   Ⓐ colorful shells.
   Ⓑ pieces of rock.
   Ⓒ tiny clear animals.
   Ⓓ people who fish near coral.

4. Which of these statements is a fact?
   Ⓐ Coral reefs have existed for millions of years.
   Ⓑ Coral may feel tough.
   Ⓒ Bad fishing methods have caused terrible harm.
   Ⓓ The biggest threat is that oceans are getting warmer.

5. In the section, "Precious Underwater Habitats," which clue word is an antonym of *sensitive*?
   Ⓐ tough
   Ⓑ bad
   Ⓒ terrible
   Ⓓ biggest

6. What causes a coral reef to lose its color and food supply?
   Ⓐ algae          Ⓒ sea grass
   Ⓑ dynamite        Ⓓ warm water

7. Scientists want to change the world's attitude. They want to change
   Ⓐ the world's temperature.
   Ⓑ the number of people in the world.
   Ⓒ how people feel and act.
   Ⓓ where people live.

8. From the details in "The Coral Reef Crisis," you can predict that unless new laws are passed,
   Ⓐ new coral will grow.
   Ⓑ coral reefs will not be saved.
   Ⓒ the oceans will get warmer.
   Ⓓ scientists will no longer study coral reefs.

9. According to "Life Abounds on Coral Reefs," how are rainforests and coral reefs alike?
   Ⓐ They both support many different kinds of life.
   Ⓑ They are both found near water.
   Ⓒ They both cover only a small part of the earth.
   Ⓓ They are both in danger.

10. Coral reefs attract sharks. Sharks
    Ⓐ are harmed by coral reefs.
    Ⓑ are drawn to coral reefs.
    Ⓒ are kept out of coral reefs.
    Ⓓ are afraid of coral reefs.

**11.** Which of these statements is an opinion?

&#9398; Thousands of species of fish live on coral reefs.

&#9399; Coral reefs attract a variety of sharks.

&#9400; Coral reefs cover less than 0.2% of the ocean floor.

&#9401; Among these are some of the most colorful fish in the world.

**12.** Which of these is a comparison called a simile?

&#9398; The coral reef is like a fine restaurant.

&#9399; Eels are long and thin.

&#9400; Wrasses eat parasites.

&#9401; Sea grasses grow in and around coral reefs.

## Extend Your Learning

- *Read About Ecosystems*

  Find and read a nonfiction book about another ecosystem, such as the rainforest, the desert, or the ocean. As you read, fill in a fact-and-opinion chart. Look over the facts and opinions in the chart and try to figure out what the author wants you to understand about the ecosystem. You can also use the details in your chart to tell classmates about the book.

- *Create a Diorama*

  In a group, plan a diorama of an ocean reef. Reread the feature stories for ideas of what to include in your diorama. You may wish to use the Internet, an encyclopedia, and other sources to learn more about the plants, animals, and structure of coral reefs. Work together to create your diorama. Then share it with the class.

- *Make a Poster*

  With a partner, do research to learn more about why coral reefs are important. Find out what young people can do to help save the coral reefs. Make a list of five ways to help save coral reefs. Then use your list to make a poster about coral reefs. Be sure to include drawings or pictures of coral reef plants and animals on your poster. Display your poster for classmates and other students to see and read.

# Identifying Author's Purpose

## Learn About Identifying Author's Purpose

*Thinking about the strategy*

Every author writes for a reason. The reason an author writes is called **author's purpose**. Authors usually write for one of four reasons.

| | |
|---|---|
| Authors write **to describe**. ▶ | They use colorful, rich details to tell about people, places, and things. |
| Authors write **to persuade**. ▶ | They try to make readers do or believe something, often by giving opinions. |
| Authors write **to entertain**. ▶ | They tell stories, using words and ideas that readers will enjoy. |
| Authors write **to explain**. ▶ | They use facts and details that help readers understand a subject. |

Authors often have more than one purpose for writing. As you read, ask yourself, "What is the author trying to do? What does the author want me to feel or know?" Be sure to pay attention to key ideas and details. This can help you identify the author's purpose.

---

*Studying a model*

Read the paragraph and the notes beside it.

*The author begins by telling about a place.*

*The author uses vivid details to tell what the place looks like.*

*The author uses more details to bring the place to life for readers.*

It hadn't rained for weeks. The ground along the long, narrow trail was bone dry and dusty. Each time the wind blew, it lifted the dull brown dust into whirls that looked like mini-twisters. The plants that lined the trail were wilted and pale from the trail dust. Even the ground squirrel that ran across the trail and disappeared in the thick brush was gray.

# Learn About a Graphic Organizer

An **author's purpose questionnaire** can help you figure out an author's purpose by answering questions that point to the author's purpose. You can use an author's purpose questionnaire to help you identify author's purpose in fiction and nonfiction selections.

Here is an author's purpose questionnaire for the paragraph on page 94. Notice how the questions focus on key ideas and details. Notice how the answers help the reader understand what the author is trying to do.

| QUESTION | ANSWER |
|---|---|
| What does the author say? | The ground along the long, narrow trail was bone dry and dusty. |
| What are key ideas and details? | It hadn't rained for weeks.<br>The wind picked up dust.<br>The plants were wilted and pale. |

*Write answers to the questions on the left.*

| | |
|---|---|
| What is the author trying to do? | The author wants the reader to "see" the dry, dusty trail. |
| **Author's Purpose** | To describe |

*Study the answers to the first two questions. Figure out what the author is trying to do. Identify the author's purpose.*

When you fill in an author's purpose questionnaire, you identify the author's purpose, or reason, for writing. This can help you understand your purpose for reading.

*The author's purpose is to describe something.*
*What is my purpose for reading?*
I want to use the details to picture the trail in my mind.

**As you read, ask yourself**

- What is the author trying to do?

- What key ideas and details point to the author's purpose?

# Learn About a Form of Writing

*Focusing on a journal entry*

A **journal entry** is usually a short piece of writing that tells about the events of one day. Some journal entries are not meant to be read by others. Other journal entries tell a story that the author enjoys sharing.

A journal entry often has these features.

- It is written in the first person, using the pronoun *I*.
- It usually describes the events of one day.
- It often tells the author's thoughts and feelings.

Here is a journal entry written by a young girl. Pay attention to the details that show what the author is thinking.

October 28, 2001

I always thought that leaves changed from green to yellow, orange, or red. Today, I learned that the leaves are yellow, orange, or red. In spring, a chemical called chlorophyll makes the leaves green. In fall, the chlorophyll disappears. Then the true colors of the leaves appear.

*Organizing ideas in an author's purpose questionnaire*

You can use an author's purpose questionnaire when reading journal entries. Here is a filled-in author's purpose questionnaire for the journal entry above.

| QUESTION | ANSWER |
|---|---|
| What does the author say? | I always thought that leaves changed from green to yellow, orange, or red. I learned that the leaves are yellow, orange, or red. |
| What are key ideas and details? | Chlorophyll makes the leaves green. When the chlorophyll disappears, the true colors of the leaves appear. |
| What is the author trying to do? | The author wants the reader to understand why leaves turn yellow, orange, or red in the fall. |
| Author's Purpose | To explain |

# Prepare for the Reading Selection

*Gaining knowledge*

On the pages that follow, you will read entries from a boy's journal. The journal entries tell about the boy's imagination. What exactly is imagination? The dictionary says that imagination is "the power to create pictures of unknown or unreal things in the mind." Using your imagination can be fun. It can take you places that you could never go in real life. Sometimes, however, the imagination and your sense of sight can play tricks on you. Together, they can make you think that you're seeing something real that is, actually, just part of your imagination.

# Learn Vocabulary

*Understanding vocabulary*

The boxed words below are **boldfaced** in the selection. Learn the meaning of each word. Then write the word that completes the sentence.

| |
|---|
| **challenged** |
| **shattered** |
| **accurate** |
| **nestled** |
| **squinted** |
| **brim** |

1. The mirror fell to the ground and _____ into many pieces.

2. I _____ when she shined the bright light in my eyes.

3. We gave a careful and _____ description of our lost puppy to the police.

4. The _____ of his cap kept the sun off his face.

5. After I won the first race, she _____ me to a second race.

6. The sleeping baby _____ in her father's arms.

Read the first part of "From the Journal of Sam Burke."

## From the Journal of Sam Burke

*Tuesday, March 24*

I should never have **challenged** Lewis to that contest. I said I could spot more wildlife than he could. What was I thinking? We live in the middle of the city! All afternoon I searched my neighborhood. I looked up trees, behind garbage cans, and near statues. All I found was leaves, trash, and lots of pigeons.

*Wednesday, March 25*

Lewis made it clear that pigeons do not count. Then I had to insist that cats don't count—even Fluffy. Lewis tried to argue that his sister's cat is quite wild, but I wouldn't give in. We also agreed that dogs, worms, squirrels, and sparrows don't count either.

*Thursday, March 26*

The strangest thing happened on the way home from school today. I was looking down at my feet when I thought I saw something move. It had a small head, tiny black eyes, and a pink tongue. It was smooth, with black and yellow stripes, and it wiggled. It was a snake!

According to the rules of our contest, I had to write down when and where I spotted an animal. I also had to draw a picture of it. It took me a while to find my notebook at the bottom of my bag. When I looked back at the snake, it was gone! Instead, all I saw was a pencil, broken in several places. It was just lying there, all black and yellow and crooked. It had a smashed pink eraser at one end and a **shattered** pencil point at the other.

*Friday, March 27*

Today, I decided to look for animals at the playground. I was sitting on a swing when suddenly, a giant butterfly appeared. It was at least six inches wide. Its colorful wings of red, green, and gold sparkled in the sun. The butterfly soared and dipped, flapping its wings like a graceful dancer.

It looked exotic, like the kind of butterfly that lives in a rainforest or jungle. This creature would certainly count! I grabbed my notebook and rose from the swing. As I got closer, the butterfly settled on a bush. I crept as near to it as I dared, keeping my eyes on its bright, colorful wings.

I opened my notebook and began sketching. I was paying close attention because I wanted to make an **accurate** drawing. When I looked up, I shook my head and blinked. Where was the butterfly?

I ran over to the bush. There was no butterfly, but **nestled** in the branches was a candy wrapper. I picked up the wrapper and tossed it into a trash can.

---

*Completing an author's purpose questionnaire*

Some of the author's purpose questionnaire has been filled in. Add more information from the first part of the journal.

| QUESTION | ANSWER |
| --- | --- |
| What does the author say? | I should never have told Lewis that I could spot more wildlife than he could. <br><br> We live in the middle of the city. |
| What are key ideas and details? | Pigeons, cats, dogs, worms, squirrels, and sparrows didn't count in the contest. <br><br> On the way home from school, I saw a snake. When I went to sketch it, it turned into a broken pencil. |
| What is the author trying to do? | |

Read the second part of "From the Journal of Sam Burke."

*Saturday, March 28*

This morning I was watching a nature program about alligators. I thought about putting an alligator in my journal. But I changed my mind. I was pretty sure that alligators on television wouldn't count even though our TV is in the city.

I decided to continue my wildlife search outdoors. When I went into my bedroom to get my notebook, I happened to look out the window.

There's a small park behind our apartment building. It has a few trees, two benches, a fountain, . . . and a tortoise? I couldn't believe it. I pressed my nose to the window and looked down. That was no small turtle. It was huge!

I could see two feet and a smooth brownish shell. I watched its head move slowly as it chewed on a patch of grass. I looked down at the tortoise for several minutes. Then I grabbed my notebook and rushed downstairs.

I ran over to the park and skidded to a halt about ten feet from the tortoise. I didn't think that tortoises were dangerous, but I didn't really want to find out. I also didn't want to think about how a giant turtle had ended up in a city park. I figured I was just lucky.

I began to draw. I **squinted** to get a clearer look. No! This couldn't be happening again. The tortoise had turned into a rock!

I dropped my notebook and ran to the rock. I slid my hands over its smooth surface. I circled the rock, looking at it from all sides. Sitting in the grass next to the rock were a pair of old, dirty sneakers. On the ground, in front of the rock was a torn baseball cap. As a breeze passed over it, the **brim** of the cap lifted and fell.

On the news tonight, there was a report of a monkey escaping from the zoo. The reporter said that it had been spotted near City Hall.

*Sunday, March 29*

The contest is over. Lewis won. He and his dad were walking near City Hall yesterday.

I don't mind that Lewis saw the monkey. If I had seen it, it probably would have turned into a fuzzy brown scarf.

I really can't explain what happened to me last week. I do know that I saw each and every one of those animals. I am sure that there was a snake on the sidewalk, an exotic butterfly at the playground, and a giant tortoise at the park. I never told Lewis about them, though.

---

*Using an author's purpose questionnaire*

Fill in the author's purpose questionnaire for the second part of the journal. Use the questionnaire that you filled in for Part One to help you identify the author's purpose for the whole selection.

| QUESTION | ANSWER |
|---|---|
| What does the author say? | |
| What are key ideas and details? | |
| What is the author trying to do? | |
| **Author's Purpose** | |

## Check Your Understanding

Think about what you've read. Then answer these questions.

1. The author wrote this journal mainly to
   - Ⓐ explain how to have a wildlife contest.
   - Ⓑ entertain readers with a story about how a contest affects one boy's imagination.
   - Ⓒ persuade readers to look for wildlife in the city.
   - Ⓓ describe different types of city wildlife.

2. Which of these details is a key to the author's purpose?
   - Ⓐ animals that turn out to be nonliving things
   - Ⓑ description of a city park
   - Ⓒ facts that tell how to set up contest rules
   - Ⓓ opinions about city animals

3. From the information in the journal, you can figure out that
   - Ⓐ pigeons are often found in a city.
   - Ⓑ there are no worms or squirrels in the city.
   - Ⓒ Sam and Lewis argue a lot.
   - Ⓓ Sam doesn't enjoy living in the city.

4. A pencil with a shattered point has a point that is
   - Ⓐ sharp.
   - Ⓒ smashed.
   - Ⓑ black.
   - Ⓓ stubby.

5. Which of these animals does Lewis see to win the contest?
   - Ⓐ wild cat
   - Ⓒ butterfly
   - Ⓑ snake
   - Ⓓ monkey

6. Which of these events happens first?
   - Ⓐ Sam thinks he sees a tortoise.
   - Ⓑ Sam watches a program about alligators.
   - Ⓒ Sam thinks he sees a huge butterfly.
   - Ⓓ Sam thinks he sees a snake.

7. Sam compares the butterfly to
   - Ⓐ a wiggling worm.
   - Ⓑ a graceful dancer.
   - Ⓒ the sparkling sun.
   - Ⓓ a giant bird.

8. What is the best meaning of the word *exotic* in the journal entry on page 99?
   - Ⓐ "bright and cheerful"
   - Ⓑ "belonging to another part of the world"
   - Ⓒ "not real"
   - Ⓓ "clear and able to see through"

9. An accurate drawing of a butterfly would
   - Ⓐ look very much like the butterfly.
   - Ⓑ show different kinds of butterflies.
   - Ⓒ be a cartoon of a butterfly.
   - Ⓓ show only one side of the butterfly.

10. When Sam squinted, he probably
    - Ⓐ bent over.
    - Ⓑ scrunched up his eyes.
    - Ⓒ drew a picture.
    - Ⓓ lifted his hand.

**11.** Why does Sam think that he's lucky to have spotted a tortoise?

- Ⓐ because it's not the time of year to see tortoises
- Ⓑ because there are no such things as tortoises
- Ⓒ because tortoises are not found in city parks
- Ⓓ because he always wanted to see a tortoise up close

**12.** Which of these events could not happen in real life?

- Ⓐ A pigeon is near a statue.
- Ⓑ Two friends have a contest.
- Ⓒ A tortoise turns into a rock.
- Ⓓ A monkey escapes from the zoo.

## Extend Your Learning

- *Read About the Imagination*

  Read an article or a story about the imagination. As you read, fill in an author's purpose questionnaire. Then use the filled-in questionnaire to identify the author's purpose for writing the article or the story.

- *Add a Journal Entry*

  In a group, look at and discuss pictures of wild animals. As you study the pictures, use your imagination to decide what kinds of objects these different animals could look like. Then write a new journal entry for "From the Journal of Sam Burke." The entry should describe a time that Sam saw a wild animal that turned out to be something else. Use the journal entries in the lesson as a guide, as well as your own imagination.

- *Write About Nature*

  With a partner, brainstorm a list of nature topics. Then together choose the same topic to write about. Decide on your purpose for writing before you begin but do not share this with your partner. You may write to describe, to persuade, to entertain, or to explain. If necessary, do research to learn more about the topic. After writing, switch papers and have your partner use an author's purpose questionnaire to figure our your purpose for writing.

# Interpreting Figurative Language

## Learn About Interpreting Figurative Language

*Thinking about the strategy*

Reading is more enjoyable when you can picture what an author is describing. An author often uses **figurative language** to help readers create pictures, or images, in their mind. Figurative language has meaning that goes beyond the usual meaning of the words.

| Figurative Language | | Example | What It Means |
| --- | --- | --- | --- |
| Simile | A simile compares two unlike things, using the word like or as. | The people below us looked like ants. | The people below appeared very small. |
| Metaphor | A metaphor compares two things without the word like or as. A metaphor says one thing is another. | The sunny day was a gift after a week of rain. | The sunny day was welcome after so much gloomy weather. |
| Idiom | An idiom uses words that together have a different meaning than the words mean by themselves. | Will you give me a hand with this heavy box? | Will you help me carry this heavy box? |

To figure out what figurative language means, think about the pictures that the words create in your mind as you read.

*Studying a model*

Read the paragraph and the notes beside it.

*The author uses similes that compare the quiet children to clams, and the sun to a bashful child.*

*The metaphor compares the sun to a globe.*

*The idiom tells me that the children got up very early.*

Annie and Hal sat on the beach, as quiet as the clams buried in the sand around them. Slowly, the sun came up. At first, it peeked above the horizon like a bashful child. Then, losing its shyness, the sun rose bright and full. Soon it was a glowing yellow globe. "Getting up before the crack of dawn was worth it," Hal whispered to Annie.

# Learn About a Graphic Organizer

*Understanding a figurative language chart*

A **figurative language chart** will help you figure out the meaning of figurative language as you read. You can use a figurative language chart to identify and figure out figurative language when reading stories, fables, poems, and other fiction and nonfiction works.

Here is a figurative language chart for the paragraph on page 104. It shows the figurative language used in the paragraph and explains what it means in ordinary language.

*List similes, metaphors, and idioms here.*

| Figurative Language | What It Means |
|---|---|
| as quiet as the clams buried in the sand around them | Annie and Hal sat on the beach without making a sound. |
| like a bashful child | The sun came up as slowly as a shy child might come into a room. |
| was a glowing yellow globe | The sun was bright and round. |
| crack of dawn | They got up very early, before the sun had begun to come up. |

*Put figurative language in your own words.*

When you complete a figurative language chart, you understand more clearly what the author wants you to see and feel as you read.

*What does the author want me to know about the beach at sunrise?*
The beach at sunrise is quiet and beautiful.

**As you read, ask yourself**

- Are these words part of a simile, a metaphor, or an idiom?
- What picture do these words create in my mind?
- How does the picture in my mind help me understand what the author is describing?

# Learn About a Form of Writing

*Focusing on a review*

A **review** tells about an event that has already taken place. The event may be a music concert, a play, a ballet, an art show, or even the circus. A good review can make readers want to attend an event. A not-so-good review may make readers skip the event.

A review often has these features.

- It briefly retells the story or the important parts of the event.
- It gives details about when and where the event took place.
- It gives the author's opinions about the event.
- It often uses figurative language to help readers picture the event.

Here is the opening paragraph of a review of a school concert.

> Last night, even the smallest members of the Young Musicians Orchestra became musical giants, especially to friends and family who watched and listened. As the first piano notes floated like twinkling lights across the darkened auditorium, the audience realized it was in for a wonderful treat.

*Organizing ideas in a figurative language chart*

You can use a figurative language chart to identify and figure out the meaning of figurative language used in a review. Here is a filled-in figurative language chart for the paragraph above.

| Figurative Language | What It Means |
|---|---|
| even the smallest members . . . became musical giants | The young musicians played so well that they sounded like famous, well-trained musicians. |
| notes floated like twinkling lights | The music sounded light and cheerful. |
| in for a wonderful treat | The audience knew that it was about to hear something pleasing and special. |

# Prepare for the Reading Selection

*Gaining knowledge*

On the following pages, you will read a review of a play. The play is based on a story by Rudyard Kipling, an English writer who lived from 1865 to 1936. Rudyard Kipling wrote hundreds of stories and set many of them in India, where he was born. Kipling's father taught school in Bombay, India, when India was under British rule. Although Kipling wrote many different kinds of narratives, he is most often remembered for his children's stories. These include *The Jungle Book*, published in 1894, and the *Just So Stories*, published in 1902. In 1907, Rudyard Kipling became the first English writer to be given the Nobel Prize for literature.

# Learn Vocabulary

*Understanding vocabulary*

The boxed words below are **boldfaced** in the selection. Learn the meaning of each word. Then write the word that means the same or nearly the same as the given word.

| | |
|---|---|
| disaster | 1. great _____ |
| production | 2. play _____ |
| fanciful | 3. actors _____ |
| audience | 4. imaginary _____ |
| cast | 5. accident _____ |
| excellent | 6. fans _____ |

Read the first part of the review "A Gem of a Show."

## A Gem of a Show

Many grade-school plays are like lovable puppies. They are cute and sweet, but they do not always do what they are supposed to do.

Yesterday, however, the third-grade class at King Elementary School showed that not every grade-school play is a **disaster** waiting to happen. In fact, the third-grade **production** of *The Elephant's Child* is a sparkling gem. Each of the young performers shines like a bright star. The set is a dream. And the costumes are **fanciful** works of art.

*The Elephant's Child* is based on a story from Rudyard Kipling's *Just So Stories*. This funny tale explains how the elephant got its long trunk. As the play opens, the Elephant has a "blackish, bulgy nose" that it can wriggle, but not use for picking things up. Then along comes the Elephant's Child who is as curious as a cat. The Elephant's Child is so curious that he can't help asking questions. He asks his aunt the Ostrich why her tail feathers grow the way they do. He asks his uncle the Giraffe why his skin is spotty. He asks his aunt the Hippopotamus why she is so large. The young elephant means no harm, but his nonstop questions are like sharp thorns. He gets on everyone's nerves, and as a result, is often in trouble. Then one day, the young elephant questions what the Crocodile has for dinner. That is when the fun and adventure of this delightful story really begin.

The students in Ms. Nam's third-grade class do a great job of bringing this comical adventure to the stage. In fact, much of the **audience** was clearly surprised by how good and funny the play is. Some couldn't believe their eyes or ears. "This was one of the best school plays I've ever seen," one woman said. Then she added, "In fact, it's one of the best plays I've ever seen."

Ms. Nam has a knack for giving direction. The young actors are clay in her hands. She has shaped them perfectly to fit their parts. The best example of this is Perry Nichols, the Elephant's Child. Perry is a breath of fresh air. From the minute he walks on stage, he has the audience under his spell.

*Completing a figurative language chart*

Fill in the figurative language chart for the first part of the review. Some examples are given. Write what you think the words mean. Then add other examples.

| Figurative Language | What It Means |
|---|---|
| like lovable puppies | A grade-school play is fun to watch, but it is usually not that good. |
| disaster waiting to happen | You can expect many things to go wrong during a grade-school play. |
| the play is a sparkling gem | The Elephant's Child is a very good play. |
| shines like a bright star | Each child actor performs very well. |
| set is a dream | |
| costumes are fanciful works of art | |
| | |
| | |
| | |
| | |
| | |

Read the second part of the review, "A Gem of a Show."

There was one nervous moment at the beginning of yesterday's show. In the opening scene, the Elephant's Child appears, wearing a short nose and great big ears that flop like wings. When Perry first came on stage, one of his ears got stuck in a side curtain. Most children would have fallen apart. Perry handled it like a pro. He tugged the ear loose, scratched his big fake ear, and sighed. The audience ate it up and gave him a big hand.

The rest of the **cast** does a great job, too. Alli Li almost steals the show as the Crocodile. A week before the play, Alli came down with a bad cold. Alli told her parents that wild horses couldn't keep her from being in the play. So, even though Alli's throat felt like sandpaper, she went on. Her voice sounded more like a bullfrog's than a crocodile's. Still, who knows what a crocodile's voice sounds like, especially a crocodile with a cold?

Alan Jenks and Richie Mann are **excellent** as the Elephant's brothers. Alan has a voice that booms like thunder. (According to some third-grade students, Ms. Nam has made Alan promise not to use this voice unless he is on stage.) On the other hand, Richie Mann's voice is a rusty tuba, rumbling and squeaky at the same time. Both boys clearly have a ball on stage.

Rounding out the cast, are Sara Prince as the Ostrich, Tyrone Jackson as the Giraffe, Thea Wilcox as the Hippopotamus, and James Wong as the Kolokolo bird. Maria Cree and Max Hamel are the narrators.

The jungle setting was created by students with the help of Mr. Withers, the art teacher. Mr. Withers told students that the stage was a blank piece of paper. It was their job to use their imaginations to turn that blank piece of paper into a jungle. The children let their imaginations run wild using cardboard, paint, crayons, and other simple materials. The result is a colorful jungle of huge leaves, thick tree trunks, and lovely flowers. The background of wild animal sounds, recorded by the class, is a nice touch.

Ms. Nam and Mr. Withers helped students to design and make their own costumes. Clearly, they again told students to let their imaginations go. The costumes are funny and clever.

*The Elephant's Child* is a bright spot of sunshine during the gray days of winter. If you missed yesterday's show, you are still in luck. The third grade will perform *The Elephant's Child* on Saturday and Sunday afternoons at 1:00 P.M. You can get tickets at the school office today and tomorrow, or at the door on the day of the show. Hurry! We hear from a little elephant that ticket lines are longer than an elephant's nose.

---

*Using a figurative language chart*

Fill in the figurative language chart with examples from the second part of the review.

| Figurative Language | What It Means |
| --- | --- |
|  |  |
|  |  |
|  |  |
|  |  |
|  |  |
|  |  |
|  |  |

## Check Your Understanding

Think about what you've read. Then answer these questions.

1. The reviewer liked the production. The reviewer liked
   - Ⓐ hearing a story.
   - Ⓑ meeting a teacher.
   - Ⓒ watching a stage show.
   - Ⓓ looking at jewelry.

2. The review does not give details about
   - Ⓐ the actors.
   - Ⓑ the set design.
   - Ⓒ how to get tickets.
   - Ⓓ the background music.

3. According to the review, why does the Elephant's Child keep getting into trouble?
   - Ⓐ He asks too many questions.
   - Ⓑ His nose is too long.
   - Ⓒ He wriggles too much.
   - Ⓓ He can't pick anything up.

4. In the review, which word is a clue to the meaning of *comical*?
   - Ⓐ good
   - Ⓑ funny
   - Ⓒ surprised
   - Ⓓ adventure

5. Which of these is an audience likely to do?
   - Ⓐ work
   - Ⓑ dance
   - Ⓒ clap
   - Ⓓ sweep

6. The words *has a knack* mean that Ms. Nam has a
   - Ⓐ talent.
   - Ⓑ hammer.
   - Ⓒ strong fist.
   - Ⓓ loud voice.

7. From the review, you can figure out that Perry
   - Ⓐ is afraid of crowds.
   - Ⓑ enjoys the fresh air.
   - Ⓒ is very clumsy.
   - Ⓓ is a natural actor.

8. Which two things are compared in the review?
   - Ⓐ a child and a curious cat
   - Ⓑ the ears of the Elephant's Child and wings
   - Ⓒ a tuba and the sound of thunder
   - Ⓓ wild horses and third-grade students

9. Which of these is a fact according to the review?
   - Ⓐ The rest of the cast does a great job.
   - Ⓑ Alli Li almost steals the show.
   - Ⓒ Alli came down with a cold.
   - Ⓓ Her voice sounded more like a bullfrog's than a crocodile's.

10. If actors are excellent, they are
    - Ⓐ lazy.
    - Ⓑ forgetful.
    - Ⓒ terrible.
    - Ⓓ great.

**11.** Which of these could not happen in real life?

Ⓐ A young elephant asks questions.

Ⓑ Perry gets a fake ear caught in a curtain.

Ⓒ Students create a colorful jungle set.

Ⓓ Teachers help students make clever costumes.

**12.** The author wrote this review mainly to

Ⓐ explain how Ms. Nam chose actors for the play.

Ⓑ convince people that they should go to see the play.

Ⓒ tell an entertaining story of how the Elephant got its nose.

Ⓓ explain why elephants have long noses.

## Extend Your Learning

- *Read a Folktale*

  Choose a different folktale, fairy tale, or fable to read with a partner. You might read the story "The Elephant's Child," or another one of Kipling's *Just So Stories*. As you read, use a figurative language chart to keep track of similes, metaphors, and idioms. After you read, work with your partner to figure out the meaning of the figurative language you listed. Discuss how understanding the figurative language helps you better understand the story.

- *Write a Review*

  As a group, choose a school program that you saw recently to review. It might be a play, a concert, a talent show, or an awards ceremony. Before you write, you may wish to reread "A Gem of a Show." Notice the figurative language that the author uses to help readers picture the play in their minds. Try to use at least one simile, one metaphor, and one idiom in your review. After you write your review, compare your ideas to those of your classmates.

- *Illustrate Figurative Language*

  Choose a simile, a metaphor, or an idiom from the story to illustrate. Divide a piece of paper in half. On one half of the paper, draw a picture that shows the actual meaning of the words. On the other half, draw a picture that shows the figurative language meaning of the words. Share and discuss your pictures with the class.

# Distinguishing Between Real and Make-believe

## Learn About Distinguishing Between Real and Make-believe

*Thinking about the strategy*

Many stories that you read are real. Many stories that you read are make-believe. A **real** story has characters, places, and events that are like characters, places, and events in real life. A **make-believe** story has characters, places, or events that could never be real.

| You can tell a story is real if | You can tell a story is make-believe if |
|---|---|
| Places are like places in real life. | Places are imaginary. |
| Characters are like people or animals in real life. | Animals talk, or people have magical powers or do impossible things. |
| Events could happen in real life. | Events could never really happen. |

Some of the stories that you read have parts that are real and parts that are make-believe. If any part of a story is make-believe, the story is make-believe.

*Studying a model*

Read the story and the notes beside it.

### Tin Soldiers in the Attic

*Young boys have remote-control toys.*

*Children do homework.*

*Children sometimes can't find their toys.*

*Tin soldiers cannot really talk to each other.*

"Ani, where is my remote-control jeep?" Lee asked his sister. Ani was at her desk, doing homework.

"I haven't got a clue," Ani answered.

While Lee talked to Ani in Ani's room, another conversation was going on in the attic.

"How did you get the jeep up here?" the one-legged tin soldier asked.

The second tin solder smiled. Rust crusted around his painted lips. "It wasn't that hard. These modern jeeps have more power than the old jeeps we used to drive."

# Learn About a Graphic Organizer

*Understanding a real/make-believe chart*

A **real/make-believe chart** will help you figure out the parts in a story that are real and the parts that are make-believe. You can use a real/make-believe chart to distinguish between real and make-believe in fairy tales, fables, tall tales, and other stories.

Here is a real/make-believe chart for the story on page 114. The chart shows the parts of the story that are real and the parts that are make-believe.

*List details in the Real column that tell what is real in the story.*

*List details in the Make-believe column that tell what is make-believe in the story.*

| **Real** *What can happen in real life* | **Make-believe** *What cannot happen in real life* |
| --- | --- |
| Lee can't find his remote-control jeep. Lee's sister Ani is doing homework at her desk. | Two tin soldiers talk to each other in the attic. A tin soldier smiles. A tin soldier drives a toy jeep. |

When you complete a real/make-believe chart, you see what is real and what is make-believe in a story. This can help you understand why things happen in the story.

*Why can't Lee find his remote-control jeep?*
A toy tin soldier has come to life and driven it up to the attic.

As you read, ask yourself

- Are the places in the story places that really exist?
- Do characters do magical or impossible things?
- Could all the events happen in real life?

115

# Learn About a Form of Writing

*Focusing on a fairy tale*

One kind of make-believe story is the **fairy tale**. Some of the first stories that you heard or read were probably fairy tales. Examples of favorite and familiar fairy tales are "Snow White and the Seven Dwarfs," "The Princess and the Pea," and "Goldilocks and the Three Bears." Like many other make-believe stories, a fairy tale may have parts that are real and parts that are make-believe.

A fairy tale also has these features.

- It is an old story that has been retold and passed down.
- It often begins with the words "once upon a time."
- It often shows a struggle between good and bad.
- It is told to entertain.

*Organizing ideas in a real/make-believe chart*

You can use a real/make-believe chart when you read a fairy tale. This will help you distinguish between the parts that are real and the parts that are make-believe in the story. Here is a filled-in real/make-believe chart for "Goldilocks and the Three Bears."

| **Real**<br>*What can happen in real life* | **Make-believe**<br>*What cannot happen in real life* |
|---|---|
| A little girl named Goldilocks lives in a far-off country.<br>Three bears live in the woods.<br>Goldilocks wanders into the woods.<br>Goldilocks goes into an empty cottage.<br>Goldilocks takes a nap.<br>Goldilocks runs home. | Three bears live in a funny little house.<br>The bears go for a walk while their soup cools off.<br>The bears have their own bowls, chairs, and beds.<br>The bears speak. |

# Prepare for the Reading Selection

*Gaining knowledge*

On the pages that follow, you will read a fairy tale by Carlo Collodi, an Italian author. Collodi is not as well known as other fairy tale writers such as the Brothers Grimm or Hans Christian Andersen. Yet, Collodi's story of "Pinocchio" is one of the most popular fairy tales of all time. Collodi's real last name was Lorenzini. He was born in Florence, Italy, in 1826, and began his writing career at age 22. He started out as a journalist. Later, he became interested in writing children's stories. *The Adventures of Pinocchio* first appeared in serial form in an Italian magazine for children. Carlo Collodi died in 1890. In 1892, M. A. Murray translated the 36 chapters of *The Adventures of Pinocchio* into English for the first time.

## Learn Vocabulary

*Understanding vocabulary*

The boxed words below are **boldfaced** in the selection. Learn the meaning of each word. Then write the word that could replace the underlined word or words in the sentence.

| | |
|---|---|
| value | 1. Uncle Charlie is healthy and as <u>lively</u> as ever. _____ |
| fright | 2. If we <u>do not obey</u>, Mom will be disappointed. _____ |
| spry | 3. That painting has no real <u>worth</u>. _____ |
| furious | 4. She was <u>very angry</u> because she saw someone throw trash in the street. _____ |
| ignored | 5. You gave me quite a <u>scare</u>. _____ |
| misbehave | 6. They <u>did not pay attention to</u> the signs and got lost. _____ |

Read the first part of the fairy tale "Pinocchio." It retells the first three chapters of Carlo Collodi's *The Adventures of Pinocchio.*

# Pinocchio

Once upon a time . . .

"There was a king!" my young readers are sure to say. "No, young readers, this story is not about a king, a queen, a princess, or a prince."

Once upon a time, there was a piece of wood.

It was a tree log of no real **value** and nothing special. At least, that is what it seemed. Somehow, this piece of wood came to be in the shop of a carpenter named Mr. Antonio. The tip of Mr. Antonio's nose was shiny, red, and round like a cherry. As a result, everyone called him Mr. Cherry.

Mr. Cherry noticed the piece of wood. "I need a new leg for my little table," he said. "That wood is just the right length. I'll use my axe to strip the bark off. Then I'll smooth the wood and carve it into the right shape."

Mr. Cherry picked up his axe. He was about to strike the wood when he heard a soft voice say, "Be careful. Don't hit me too hard."

Mr. Cherry looked around the shop. He saw his bench, a closed cabinet, and sawdust on the floor. Where had the voice come from? "Surely, I'm hearing things!" he exclaimed. With that, he struck the wood with the axe.

"Ouch! That hurt me!" the soft little voice cried.

This time, Mr. Cherry dropped the axe. He plopped into a chair and stared at the piece of wood in **fright**. "Wood cannot talk," he said. "My imagination is going wild."

Mr. Cherry picked up his plane to smooth and polish the piece of wood.

"Please, quit it! You're tickling me!" It was that same little voice.

Mr. Cherry fell to the floor in a faint. Stars danced and twinkled around his head. When Mr. Cherry woke, he noticed that his cherry red nose was now blue from fright. At the same moment, he heard a knock at the door. "Come in," Mr. Cherry said, glad to have company.

A **spry** old man named Geppetto came into the shop. Children often teased Geppetto and called him Polendina. That's because he wore a bright yellow wig that looked like *polenta*, a porridge, or yellow corn meal mush.

Geppetto told Mr. Cherry that he needed some wood to make a puppet. "I will make my beautiful puppet dance, fence, and do tricks," Geppetto said eagerly. "I will put on puppet shows around the world to earn my living."

Mr. Cherry knew just the wood to give Geppetto. But, as he was handing the piece of wood to Geppetto, it kicked Geppetto in the leg and whispered, "Polendina."

Geppetto was **furious**. He thought his old friend Mr. Cherry had dropped the wood on his leg on purpose and then called him a name. The two men got into a terrible argument. After the fight ended, Mr. Cherry and Geppetto shook hands. They made a promise to be friends forever. Then Geppetto left the shop with his piece of wood.

---

*Completing a real/ make-believe chart*    Add more details to the real/make-believe chart to tell what is real and what is make-believe in the first part of the fairy tale.

| **Real** <br> *What can happen in real life* | **Make-believe** <br> *What cannot happen in real life* |
|---|---|
| Mr. Antonio is a carpenter. <br> A tree log is in Mr. Antonio's shop. | The piece of wood speaks. |

Read the second part of the fairy tale "Pinocchio."

Geppetto hurried home. Before he began to carve the wood, he thought up a name for his puppet. "I will call him Pinocchio. This name is sure to bring him good luck," he said. Then he started whittling away.

The first thing he carved was the puppet's hair. Then he made the forehead. Next, he created the puppet's eyes. As soon as the eyes were made, the eyes blinked. Then they stared at Geppetto. This made Geppetto nervous. "Why are you staring at me like that?" Geppetto said. There was no reply.

Then Geppetto carved Pinocchio's nose. Geppetto stopped, but the nose did not. It kept growing and growing and growing. Geppetto tried to shorten it. But as soon as he cut off the end, the nose grew long again. Finally, Geppetto gave up and moved on to the puppet's mouth. The mouth was not even finished, when it laughed at poor Geppetto.

"Stop making fun of me!" Geppetto cried. "Stop laughing!"

The mouth stopped laughing. Instead, it stuck out its tongue at Geppetto. The old man **ignored** the naughty puppet and kept carving.

Geppetto's problems were not over. As he finished Pinocchio's hands, the puppet grabbed Geppetto's wig and plunked it onto his own wooden head. "You are not even a whole puppet yet, and you **misbehave**," Geppetto said sadly. "Don't you know that you are to respect your papa?"

Geppetto carved the rest of Pinocchio's body. Finally, he carved the legs and feet. The ungrateful puppet kicked Geppetto on the nose. "I should have been more careful," Geppetto said. Then he placed Pinocchio on the floor to show him how to walk. At first, the wooden legs were stiff and could not move. But Geppetto patiently and lovingly showed Pinocchio what to do.

What did Pinocchio do to thank Geppetto?

He ran out of the little house and down the street!

Geppetto would never have caught Pinocchio. The puppet ran as fast as a trained racehorse. However, it so happened that a police officer was nearby. He heard Geppetto shout, "Stop him!" The officer blocked Pinocchio's way.

Geppetto caught up to Pinocchio. He scolded him. He would have grabbed him by the ears, but Geppetto forgot to carve ears. So he grabbed Pinocchio's collar. By then a crowd had gathered. They began to shout that Geppetto was mean and cruel and did not deserve such a fine boy. The police officer set Pinocchio free, and the puppet ran off.

"This is all my fault," Geppetto said. "I should have carved a well-behaved puppet."

*After he leaves Geppetto, Pinocchio has many adventures. He makes many mistakes that show him what it means to be good and kind. This helps make him a real boy.*

---

*Using a real/make-believe chart*

Fill in the real/make-believe chart with details from the second part of the fairy tale.

| **Real** <br> *What can happen in real life* | **Make-believe** <br> *What cannot happen in real life* |
| --- | --- |
| | |

## Check Your Understanding

Think about what you've read. Then answer these questions.

1.  The tree log had no value so it
    - Ⓐ had no bark on it.
    - Ⓑ was not worth anything.
    - Ⓒ was too short to be of use.
    - Ⓓ would not burn well.

2.  Mr. Antonio is called Mr. Cherry because he
    - Ⓐ eats cherries all the time.
    - Ⓑ makes furniture out of cherry wood.
    - Ⓒ has a nose like a cherry.
    - Ⓓ is always happy.

3.  Mr. Cherry faints from fright. He faints because he is
    - Ⓐ afraid.
    - Ⓑ weak.
    - Ⓒ hungry.
    - Ⓓ hurt.

4.  From the details, you can figure out that Geppetto does not like
    - Ⓐ corn meal mush.
    - Ⓑ Mr. Cherry.
    - Ⓒ puppets that do tricks.
    - Ⓓ his nickname Polendina.

5.  In Part One, which clue word is a synonym of *argument*?
    - Ⓐ purpose
    - Ⓑ promise
    - Ⓒ shop
    - Ⓓ fight

6.  Which of these could really happen?
    - Ⓐ A piece of wood talks.
    - Ⓑ A piece of wood is ticklish.
    - Ⓒ Two men promise to be friends forever.
    - Ⓓ Stars dance and twinkle around a man's head.

7.  How does the puppet misbehave?
    - Ⓐ It walks stiffly.
    - Ⓑ It sticks out its tongue.
    - Ⓒ It smiles.
    - Ⓓ It blinks its eyes.

8.  Geppetto forgets to carve Pinocchio's
    - Ⓐ ears.　　Ⓒ legs.
    - Ⓑ mouth.　Ⓓ eyes.

9.  Which of these events happens last?
    - Ⓐ Geppetto names his puppet Pinocchio.
    - Ⓑ Geppetto scolds Pinocchio.
    - Ⓒ The puppet grabs Geppetto's wig.
    - Ⓓ A police officer hears Geppetto shout, "Stop him!"

10. You can tell that this is a make-believe story because
    - Ⓐ a man comes to a carpenter's shop for a piece of wood.
    - Ⓑ a man carves a puppet from wood.
    - Ⓒ a puppet comes to life.
    - Ⓓ a crowd of people gather in the street.

**11.** How is Pinocchio like some other children?

Ⓐ He is made of wood.

Ⓑ His nose keeps growing and growing.

Ⓒ He cannot talk.

Ⓓ He does not always obey.

**12.** The author wrote the fairy tale mainly to

Ⓐ explain how to carve a puppet from wood.

Ⓑ entertain readers with a story about Pinocchio.

Ⓒ describe what it feels like to be a puppet like Pinocchio.

Ⓓ persuade readers to obey their parents.

## Extend Your Learning

• *Read and Retell a Make-believe Story*

Read another fairy tale or a story that contains make-believe. Use a real/make-believe chart to make notes about what is real and what is make-believe in the story. Then use your filled-in chart to retell the story to a partner.

• *Write a Make-believe Story*

With a group, write a new adventure for Pinocchio, or continue the story "Tin Soldiers in the Attic," on page 114. Brainstorm ideas for where your story will take place, who will be in it, and what will happen. Use a real/make-believe chart or a story map to plan your story. Then write your story and draw pictures to go with it. Share your story with other groups.

• *Make Puppets and Put on a Play*

Make paper-bag or stick puppets for the characters in "Pinocchio." You can look in how-to books or on the Internet for directions. Look over the story for details that describe what the characters look like. Use these details to help create each puppet. You and your classmates may wish to use your puppets to put on a play about Pinocchio.

## Reading Selection One

Read the article "Before They Were President."

### Before They Were President

What do a rancher, a real-estate salesman, a miner, a peanut farmer, an actor, a tailor, and a football player all have in common? Give up? Each of these workers one day became president of the United States.

Theodore Roosevelt spent two years as a rancher in the Dakota Territory. Roosevelt loved the land. When he became president in 1901, he worked hard to protect our forests and natural resources. As a result, many people called him the conservation president.

Ulysses Grant was our eighteenth president. He once worked as a real-estate salesman. Unfortunately, Grant was not a very good salesman.

Herbert Hoover, who was president from 1929 to 1933, once worked as a gold miner in California and Australia.

Jimmy Carter, who was in office from 1977 to 1981, was a peanut farmer. After he left office, he wanted to help needy people in America. Today, he and his wife Rosalynn help build houses for people who cannot afford houses.

Several presidents were once in the news and entertainment business. Warren Harding, our twenty-ninth president, owned and edited a newspaper in Ohio. Lyndon Johnson became president in 1963. Johnson owned a radio station in Texas. Ronald Reagan, our fortieth president, was a sportscaster and a movie star.

Some presidents were in the fashion business. Andrew Johnson was a tailor before he became president in 1865. Harry Truman, president from 1945 to 1953, owned a men's clothing store in Kansas City.

Two presidents were football players. Our thirty-fourth president, Dwight Eisenhower, was a star football player at West Point Military Academy. And Gerald Ford, president from 1974 to 1977, played football for the University of Michigan. Ford later coached football and boxing at Yale University.

## Check Your Understanding

Think about what you've read. Then answer these questions.

1.  The article is mostly about
    - Ⓐ what presidents do after they are no longer president.
    - Ⓑ the jobs some presidents had before becoming president.
    - Ⓒ why some men become president.
    - Ⓓ how hard presidents work.

2.  Why was Theodore Roosevelt called the conservation president?
    - Ⓐ He was a rancher in the Dakota Territory.
    - Ⓑ He loved the land.
    - Ⓒ He worked to protect our forests.
    - Ⓓ He was once a farmer.

3.  Which of these is an opinion?
    - Ⓐ Ulysses Grant was our eighteenth president.
    - Ⓑ Ulysses Grant was not a very good salesman.
    - Ⓒ Herbert Hoover was president from 1929 to 1933.
    - Ⓓ Herbert Hoover once worked as a gold miner in California.

4.  Which president worked for the needy after leaving office?
    - Ⓐ Jimmy Carter
    - Ⓑ Warren Harding
    - Ⓒ Lyndon Johnson
    - Ⓓ Harry Truman

5.  In the article, which word gives a clue to the meaning of the word *fashion*?
    - Ⓐ future
    - Ⓑ president
    - Ⓒ business
    - Ⓓ clothing

6.  In what way were Dwight Eisenhower and Gerald Ford alike?
    - Ⓐ They both were generals.
    - Ⓑ They both coached boxing.
    - Ⓒ They both played football.
    - Ⓓ They both went to Yale University.

7.  From the article, you can tell
    - Ⓐ Ulysses Grant was always successful.
    - Ⓑ Jimmy Carter knows a lot about growing peanuts.
    - Ⓒ Ronald Reagan did not enjoy acting.
    - Ⓓ Andrew Johnson made all his own clothes.

8.  Which of these men was president last?
    - Ⓐ Warren Harding
    - Ⓑ Dwight Eisenhower
    - Ⓒ Ulysses Grant
    - Ⓓ Ronald Reagan

9.  From the article, you can predict that future presidents will all
    - Ⓐ have different backgrounds.
    - Ⓑ be interested in sports.
    - Ⓒ have worked on the land.
    - Ⓓ have owned their own businesses.

10. The author wrote the article mainly to
    - Ⓐ persuade readers that anyone can be president.
    - Ⓑ tell an entertaining story about Theodore Roosevelt.
    - Ⓒ explain what some men did before becoming president.
    - Ⓓ describe what it feels like to be elected president.

Read the fable "Country Mouse and City Mouse."

### Country Mouse and City Mouse

A simple country mouse received a postcard from her sophisticated cousin who lived in the city. The note on the card read:

Dear Cousin,

    I am planning a vacation this fall. I've never been to the country. I can't help but wonder why it is so special to you. Could I come for a visit?

Yours truly,

City Mouse

Country Mouse quickly dashed off a reply to her cousin that said, "Autumn is a lovely time to visit. Please come."

To prepare for her cousin's visit, Country Mouse gathered extra nuts and berries. She also collected scraps of stale bread and dried bits of bacon.

Country Mouse was proud of her small, simple home, which she kept neat and clean. When City Mouse arrived, Country Mouse welcomed him with great pleasure. She did not notice when City Mouse stuck up his nose at the plain surroundings. Nor did she notice when City Mouse frowned at the supper placed before him.

"Is this the best that you eat?" City Mouse asked after they had eaten.

Country Mouse had heartily enjoyed her dinner. "What is wrong with this food?" she asked, puzzled.

"Nothing, I suppose," City Mouse said. "It's just that, well, we city mice are used to better."

That evening after dinner, the two cousins went for a walk through the neighboring meadow. "It's so quiet here," City Mouse complained. "Don't you ever long for excitement?"

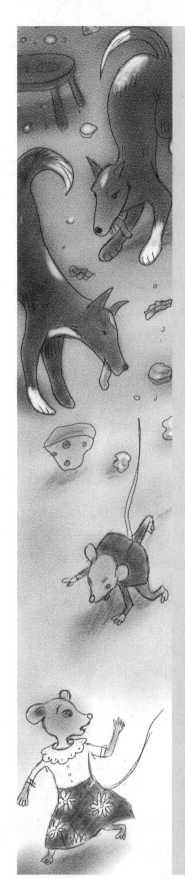

"No," Country Mouse answered honestly.

"Visit me during the winter holidays," City Mouse said. "You will see that life does not have to be so dull."

Country Mouse was a bit curious. City Mouse did make city life sound exciting. "All right," she said. "I'll come."

Two months later, Country Mouse made the journey to the city. Tired and cold after hours of traveling, Country Mouse knocked on City Mouse's door.

"Come in, come in," City Mouse said politely. "How was your trip? You must be tired! Let's have something to eat and drink." City Mouse led Country Mouse into a large and beautiful dining room.

Country Mouse's jaw fell when she saw the dining room table. "That's the longest table I've ever seen," she said. "And I have never seen so much food in all my life."

"Help yourself," City Mouse said. Soon the cousins were dining on cakes, cookies, jams, fancy nuts, and lots of other fine food.

All at once, Country Mouse heard loud, fierce growling. "What was that?" she said in a frightened voice.

City Mouse did not seem worried. "Oh, that's just the family dogs," he said. Just then, two huge dogs ran into the room. "Run!" City Mouse hollered.

"Dogs!" Country Mouse cried, when the two were safe. "You have to go about your home in fear of hungry dogs! And you think you live better than I do. Well, I'd rather have less to eat and live in peace."

Like a streak of lightning, Country Mouse bolted out the door of City Mouse's fancy home. She did not stop running until she was back in the country, in her safe and simple home.

## Check Your Understanding

Think about what you've read. Then answer these questions.

**11.** What is the best meaning of the word *sophisticated* in the fable?
- Ⓐ "plain and simple"
- Ⓑ "not well-educated"
- Ⓒ "wise and worldly"
- Ⓓ "easy to anger"

**12.** From the fable, you can figure out that Country Mouse
- Ⓐ is not fussy about food.
- Ⓑ does not like the quiet.
- Ⓒ has no friends.
- Ⓓ is messy.

**13.** Which of these events could really happen?
- Ⓐ A mouse sends a postcard to his cousin.
- Ⓑ Two mice eat nuts.
- Ⓒ A mouse frowns at his supper.
- Ⓓ Two mice talk as they walk through a meadow.

**14.** Why does Country Mouse agree to visit City Mouse?
- Ⓐ She is tired of the country.
- Ⓑ She doesn't want to hurt her cousin's feelings.
- Ⓒ She loves to travel.
- Ⓓ She's curious about city life.

**15.** How is City Mouse's house different from Country Mouse's house?
- Ⓐ City Mouse's house is fancy.
- Ⓑ City Mouse's house is small.
- Ⓒ City Mouse's house is quiet.
- Ⓓ City Mouse's house is clean.

**16.** When Country Mouse first arrives at City Mouse's house, she is surprised by
- Ⓐ the two angry dogs.
- Ⓑ how cold the house is.
- Ⓒ the size of the table.
- Ⓓ how small the house is.

**17.** Which of these events happens last?
- Ⓐ City Mouse sends a postcard to Country Mouse.
- Ⓑ Country Mouse visits the city.
- Ⓒ City Mouse hollers, "Run."
- Ⓓ Country Mouse and City Mouse walk in the meadow.

**18.** Which of these contains a simile?
- Ⓐ I'd rather live in peace.
- Ⓑ She ran like a streak of lightning.
- Ⓒ You go about your home in fear.
- Ⓓ He did not seem worried.

**19.** From the fable, you can predict that
- Ⓐ City Mouse will never write to Country Mouse again.
- Ⓑ Country Mouse will move to the city.
- Ⓒ City Mouse will move to the country.
- Ⓓ Country Mouse will never go to City Mouse's house again.

**20.** The author wrote this fable mainly to
- Ⓐ get people to move to the country.
- Ⓑ entertain readers with a story that also teaches a lesson.
- Ⓒ explain why mice are afraid of dogs.
- Ⓓ describe what mice eat.